The Microwave Diet

Clare Ferguson

THE MICROWAVE DIET

CLARE FERGUSON

PHOTOGRAPHY BY DAVID GILL

CONRAN OCTOPUS

To all cooks
whose microwave sits
lonely and unused
in a corner of the kitchen.

First published in 1994 by
Conran Octopus Limited
37 Shelton Street
London WC2H 9HN

Designer: Alyson Kyles
Project Editor: Louise Simpson
Editor: Norma Macmillan
Stylist: Helen Payne
Food Stylist: Clare Ferguson
Editorial Assistant: Jane Chapman
Production: Mano Mylvaganam

A CIP record for this book is available from
the British Library

ISBN 1 85029 549 2

Printed and bound in Hong Kong

★ Use metric or imperial measures – don't change from
one to the other.

★ All spoon measures are level and ingredients are at
room temperature.

★ The calorie count for these recipes has been calculated
using *McCance & Widdowson's: The Composition of Foods*
by A. A. Paul & D. A. T. Southgate, HMSO;
DIET-PRO, computer program by Lifestyle Software
Group; and manufacturers' figures.

CONTENTS

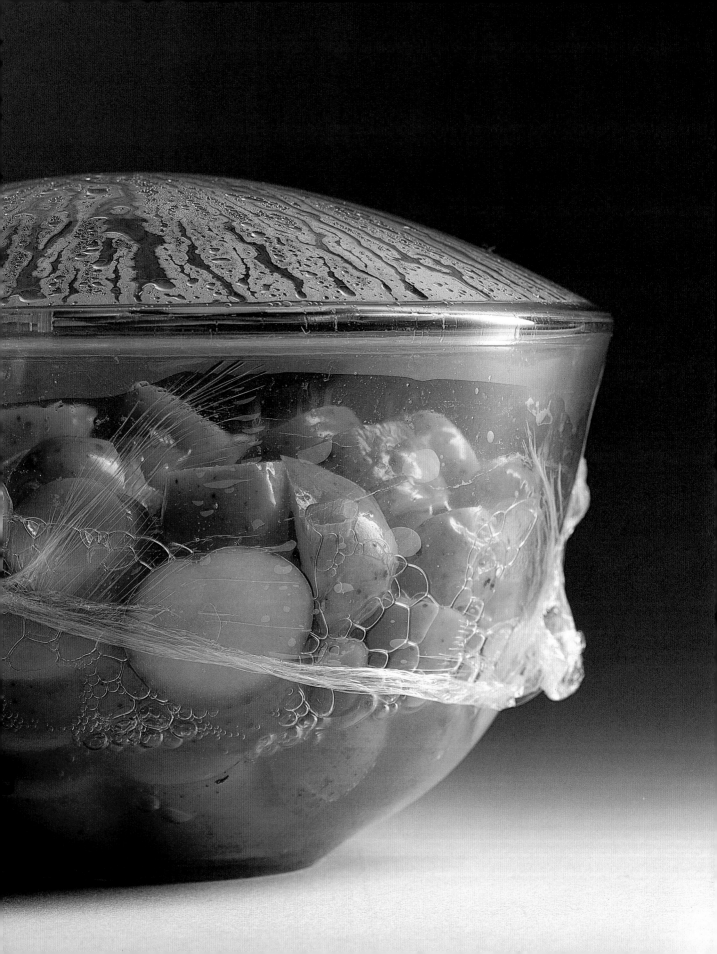

MICROWAVE MYTHS, DIET & MAGIC

A good cook is an eternal apprentice, and it takes time and skill to master new techniques. The microwave is the biggest revolution in cooking since the baker's oven came indoors. It can open up new possibilities, simplify cooking, save time and minimize mess. It also saves the world's energy resources because it is highly fuel efficient. Microwaves cook many foods brilliantly. Reheating and defrosting are only two of the minor functions. But far too many people equate the microwave with second-rate eating, sloppy cooking habits, poor flavour and production-line meals. How much they are missing!

Sixty per cent of this country's kitchens now contain a microwave cooker. Even so, many of their owners still have to be dragged kicking and screaming towards any sort of microwave know-how. Fear of the new lurks deep in our collective psyche. To relearn a process, especially an old familiar one like cooking, makes us feel insecure, so we deride the new idea instead.

This book aims to set the misconceptions right. It's magical to cook a poppadum without any fat in seconds, make real soup in minutes, bring strawberries to a scarlet perfection in a syrup perfumed with summer's vivid scents. Most people would like to create healthy snacks quickly, sizzle fish in under 3 minutes, cook rice that doesn't stick or lump, speed up simple pudding recipes, speed-cook soups and root vegetables, make a hot salad in a few minutes, and invent sensational sauces without a saucepan. The microwave can do all this.

Lots of the dishes here, I must confess, I was rarely prepared to bother with before I became familiar with my microwave. Now I am addicted to them. They are easy and rewarding and I make them often, usually without recipes. With practice it is easy to guess, so experiment and enjoy yourself.

THE HEALTH ISSUES

Microwaves, good eating, good cooking and good health can be closely linked – just by using the basic, single-function, first-generation microwave cooker that sits virtually unused in most kitchens. Asparagus cooks with almost no water so that its own true flavours do not wash away. Salmon kebabs with a sassy salsa or red mullet fillets in paper are ready to eat, looking and tasting lovely, in under 5 minutes. Tender veal blanquette develops a particularly suave sauce with no cream. Aubergines, normally time-consuming and oil-absorbing, cook rapidly 'au naturel' with intriguing new colour. Baby potatoes, packed in a microwave oven bag, are infused with mint and fat-free. Brown rice, barley and porridge, quick-cooked and easy, take on new identities – worth eating for a healthy change. An icecream glamorous enough for any party contains only 188 calories per generous serving. Recipes like these are what make up the Microwave Diet. Just as microwave cooking is misunderstood, with all sorts of idiocies blamed on this useful machine rather than on the user, so the word 'diet' is mistakenly always interpreted as a 'slimming diet' when it really just means a list or selection of foods or dishes. In fact, a diet can be slimming or fattening, healthy or unhealthy.

The Microwave Diet comprises healthy recipes that are geared to weight loss, but which, above all, promote well being. Each recipe is cooked solely using a microwave, which ensures the maximum retention of valuable nutrients: microwave radiation gets effectively to the food without the need for an intermediate substance or process (no boiling water for steam, no hot oil in a preheated metal pan, no preheated oven walls for hot air).

Many fruits, vegetables and fish cook well whole, so there's less cut surface to lose vitamins by leaching. Many foods are served and eaten in their natural skin that was designed to seal in the nutrients. Much less cooking water is used, so nutrients are not leached out and discarded. And efficient microwave reheating reduces any vitamin loss by heat to the minimum.

Look at some of the evidence. If you compare the vitamin C in potatoes before and after cooking by various methods, the results look something like this: vitamin C retained after microwave cooking is 82 per cent; after cooking in an ordinary steamer, 41 per cent; bamboo steamer, 47 per cent; pressure cooker, 37 per cent; convection oven, 26 per cent; and finally, boiled normally in a saucepan, only 40 per cent. Draw your own conclusions.

With microwave cooking, true food tastes are better preserved. This means far fewer calories

because much less fat, sugar and rich sauces are needed to compensate for the usual flavour losses. Many microwaved foods taste great with just a final sprinkle of herbs, a squeeze of lemon, a blob of low-fat yogurt. And poached fruit requires no heavy sugar syrup. So the microwave can make many less healthy cooking methods obsolete.

We need dietary fibre daily to speed the waste products of digestion through the lower gut. Soluble fibres cook so effectively in the microwave that the foods not only taste great but also set to a delectable natural jelly. Insoluble fibre – fruit skins, pith, husks, vegetable membranes, etc. – cooks superbly in a fraction of the usual time.

In addition to all these health benefits, a microwave will also set you free – free to leave the kitchen, that is. Down with kitchen captivity – haunting the oven door to check if the roast is done, guarding the grill or deep fat fryer to prevent a kitchen bonfire. The microwave allows you to cook so easily it's almost embarrassing. You push buttons and walk away. And you're out of the 'snack-food danger zone', so less temptation, fewer calories.

New fruit and vegetable sauces (fiddly to make, pre-microwave) can now take pride of place; butter and cream take a back seat. Bright colours stay bright, clear fresh tastes stay true: imagine a scarlet salmon and red pepper sauce over pasta, a green salad followed by fresh strawberries with hot mango and lime sauce, made in just a few minutes. This low-calorie but delicious supper takes well under an hour. A kitchen revelation is in store for you.

CONTROL & VERSATILITY

Microwave cookers heat (and therefore cook) food. Depending on how you heat food (in steam, in fat, on a dry, preheated metal surface, in hot dry air, poached in bubbling syrup, or even under the ground between hot stones) the flavour and the look will vary. It will be more (or less) tender or firm; less (or more) crusty or soft; somewhat (or a lot) changed in colour or not at all; caramelized and brown or utterly pale.

We have become used to many traditionally cooked foods having a recognizable crunch, a crustiness or a browned surface. But these are not always essential. They are just familiar, and we have grown afraid of change. The microwave process and its speediness keep a special sort of freshness, vividness and truer-to-the-original taste.

A first-generation, single-function microwave cooker doesn't produce the crusty baked potatoes which your traditional oven does. However, what you will get is soft-skinned, creamy-fleshed potato, full of vitamin-high, 100 per cent potato flavour. You won't even need butter, just some black pepper. And it will take minutes to cook, not hours.

For many foods such simplicity will work a treat. But for others it just doesn't, and the traditional cooking methods are needed to give the desirable flavour, colour, texture and 'mouth feel'.

The microwave cooker does have other drawbacks. It doesn't deal well with large quantities. It can easily ruin the texture of some foods (overcooked croissants become like concrete). And though it leaves some foods sexily pale (veal blanquette, for example), other foods can look anaemic, unfamiliar and odd, needing a herb, nut or spice topping to camouflage them.

But a microwave is much more than just an oven: it can poach, boil, steam and griddle-cook, as well as bake, stew and roast. It can dry herbs, make jam, sterilize jars. I have deliberately called it a 'microwave *cooker*'. It bakes, yes, but is used much more like a hob – a fact that is important because it changes your appreciation of what a microwave can do for you.

You decide on a time, you press a button. The beauty is that the beeper will sound and the obedient machine ALWAYS TURNS ITSELF OFF. So simple! Why isn't this fact blazed across the heavens? Believe me, this is a revolutionary bonus. Residual heat will also keep the food hot, continue its cooking (at no extra power cost) during a 'cook-on' time or standing time. You can leave and then return. You are in control.

SAFE & EFFICIENT MICROWAVE USE

Active people, yachties, caravanners, student cooks on budgets – all find microwave cookers a boon. And it is not only the disabled, partially sighted, the elderly and very young who value the safety and convenience of microwave cooking. The space-saving versatility and cleanness make a microwave cooker a natural for most busy households. Some basic rules should be noted.

Safety
- Do not obstruct the vent or door opening.
- When moving the microwave, always keep the door shut and the machine level.
- Running an empty machine damages the magnetron. Avoid it. The only time it is correct to do so is when preheating a browning dish.
- Wipe up spills as they occur.
- Be careful opening roasting bags and stirring hot liquids. Remove coverings away from you and don't lean over hot food while stirring.
- Custards, drinks, sauces, syrups and some dense foods like potatoes or apples retain a lot of heat. Don't burn your mouth: wait a little. Allow at least 1 minute's extra standing time (even if not specified), if in doubt.

Metal
- Microwaves cannot pass through metal (even some painted plate borders), so bounce off it. Sparks and bright light (arcing) happen. Damage to the interior of the cooker may result.
- Never cook food in metal containers. Do not use metal tops or metal skewers.
- Avoid sealing roasting bags with metal ties. Use plastic ties, string or rubber bands.
- Aluminium foil (in small amounts only) can protect or shield thin parts of foods which would otherwise overcook. Add the foil shield near the start or end of cooking. Avoid direct contact between the foil and the top, sides or bottom of the cooker.
- Second-generation 'multi-cooker' and 'combination' microwaves may permit some use of metal utensils. Follow the instructions for your machine.
- Only use a thermometer after cooking stops, not during cooking. (The exception is a specialist microwave thermometer.)

Shielding the thin end of the lamb with foil prevents over-cooking. The foil must rest on a dish and not touch the microwave oven itself.

MICROWAVE POWER

Look at the front of your microwave cooker. Since 1992 the power of microwave cookers has been rated using an internationally agreed standard method called IEC 705. These microwaves are now labelled with a symbol ⬚. Top right gives the power output in WATTS and in the bottom right corner a letter between A & E gives the heating category, based on the microwave's capacity to heat small food packs and 'microwave-ready-meals' (not the subject of this book). Your microwave's instruction manual should explain this as it applies to your particular model. Pre-1992 microwaves had their power rated by the manufacturer and the stated power output may vary from the current IEC 705 ratings. The difference may be between 50 and 150 WATTS. Your supplier will be able to tell you the new IEC 705 rating for your microwave. It is also useful to send off for the free booklet *The New Microwave Labels* (No. PB0779) from: Food Sense, London SE99 7TT.

Here are some examples of the old manufacturer's ratings compared with the new IEC 705 ratings:

	OLD POWER RATING	NEW **IEC** RATING
Toshiba ER9630EW	650W	750W
Zanussi MW700	700W	750W
Sanyo EM3415	700W	700W
Sharp R8R10	700W	800W
Neff 6270/5	700W	800W
Hitachi MR7990	710W	750W

The recipes in this book were tested on a pre-1992 model, 700 WATT microwave which is now rated at 750 WATTS under the IEC 705 ratings. This microwave has no turntable but instead uses a 'stirrer device' to distribute the microwave energy evenly. It has a large oven capacity, 1.3 cubic feet, and digital controls. Microwave power is mostly used on high or full but it can be reduced to various lower settings for casseroling or gentle cooking etc. Your manual will give the settings for your particular model.

In this book I have used:

HIGH:	100% power	MEDIUM:	50–60% power
LOW:	30% power	VERY LOW:	10% power

TIMING

The times in this book are based on a 750 WATT (IEC rating) microwave. Higher-powered cookers will require slightly less time and lower-powered cookers slightly more time. If you have a microwave with a different wattage, this simple chart shows you the number of seconds per minute of cooking time you will have to add/subtract for the recipes in the book:

IEC RATING	COOKING ADJUSTMENT TIME
850 WATTS	subtract 10 seconds per minute
800 WATTS	subtract 5 seconds per minute
750 WATTS	NO CHANGE
700 WATTS	add 5 seconds per minute
650 WATTS	add 10 seconds per minute
600 WATTS	add 15 seconds per minute

Cross-cutting tomatoes helps prevent the skin from splitting whilst cooking. Even spacing around the outside edge of the dish also helps even heat distribution.

Make a series of parallel cuts with a sharp knife along the length of a Frankfurter sausage to keep it in shape and prevent it from bursting.

Different microwaves have different features as do traditional ovens. Frequent use will make you adept with any idiosyncrasies, but here are a few points to start with:

- Always undercook, then cook again. Don't overcook.
- Microwave cooking is more about cooking by time than temperature, and then by taste and observation.
- As soon as the door is opened the mechanism automatically stops. Open and close the door whenever you wish to see how the food feels, smells and looks. When the door closes cooking will continue until the preset time is up.
- For these recipes assume that all foods begin cooking at room temperature unless otherwise stated. The temperature of the food (room temperature or chilled), its size and shape, the size and shape of the cooking dish, and whether the dish is covered or uncovered will all affect cooking and timings.
- For adjustments of the food during cooking (to even up cooking and prevent any hotspots), set the timer for the shorter time, then make the adjustment and reset the timer each time until the full recipe time is up.

Streamlining the cooking process
- Evenly spaced foods (in a ring) cook most evenly.
- Evenly shaped foods also cook most evenly. If there is a thick/dense end put that towards the outside and the thinner/more porous part in the centre.
- Skins and membranes must be slashed or pierced to avoid steam build-up.

- Hot, thick dense liquids need careful stirring (sides to centre) or whisking (away from the face) to prevent steam build-up and boil-overs.
- Microwaves penetrate food to 5cm/2in depth all over (top, sides, base) so that any food less than 10cm/4in thick starts to cook very quickly.
- The more food that is cooked at any one time, the longer the cooking time.

Cooking times: cooking by numbers
- The higher the wattage, the faster the cooking time.
- HIGH (100%) power is twice as fast as MEDIUM (50%) power.
- Large amounts of food and liquid take more time than smaller. (Large volumes of water must be pre-boiled, e.g. for pasta.)
- Dense foods take longer than airy light foods.
- High-fat, high-sugar foods cook fastest and hottest.
- Finely chopped foods (such as minced pork) cook faster than large chunks (such as casserole veal).
- Solid items need turning over or repositioning from sides to centre to keep cooking even and quick.

Standing time
- Food continues to cook for some minutes after the microwave stops. This 'cook-on' or 'standing' time is useful. It helps even up heat and tenderness, helps dry off cake tops, deepens the colour of browned meats, and crisps up crunchy surfaces.
- Standing time can take place in the turned-off cooker, or once the food is removed. Keep it hot by tenting it with foil.

Baked apples should be slashed around their diameter then cored to allow most even penetration of microwave energy and heat.

Pierce both the yolk and the white membrane carefully several times with a fine point – such as a needle or a skewer – to keep the egg in shape.

COOKING UTENSILS & MATERIALS

Many existing items from your kitchen may be fine for microwave cooking. These include:

- Wide-bottomed bowls, dishes and measuring jugs made from Pyrex, heat-resistant glass, china, porcelain and non-metallic glazed pottery (not earthenware).
- Roasting bags (nylon), greaseproof paper, baking parchment, kitchen paper (but not recycled paper) and paper napkins are all useful.
- Cardboard plates, paper cups; wood, cane and non-synthetic fabric cloths (brief reheats only).
- Oval and round china pots (ramekins) about 150ml/¼ pint volume.
- Pyrex or toughened glass plates (these make good lids for bowls instead of clingfilm).
- Non-metal casseroles (round or oval cook better and more evenly than square or rectangular ones). Corners of square dishes or the ends of oblong ones should be 'foil-shielded' to prevent overcooking in these areas.
- The ideal shape for microwave cooking is a ring-shaped dish with handles for easy lifting. Use these for most purposes.

Special microwave items worth buying

Many of the recipes in this book were created and cooked in the following specialist utensils. Please follow recipe-specified sizes and shapes for best microwave results. Dimensions do matter.

- Clear Pyrex measuring jugs with sloping sides, rounded internally at the bottom; small (600ml/ 1 pint); medium (1 litre/1¾ pints); and very large (2 litres/3½ pints).
- Opaque white, microwave-proof plastic jug: 1.3 litres/2¼ pint volume.
- Glazed white china ridged roasting utensil.
- Microwave-proof plastic ridged bacon rack and base.
- Round, white oven-to-table glass-ceramic casserole dishes with clear glass lids: small, medium and large.
- Browning dishes or 'browners' (square and circular) with clear glass lids. The largest size is most versatile.
- Microwave-proof plastic (fish) steamer with pierced inset and vented, see-through plastic lid.
- Microwave-proof pasta cooker with inset drainer, fold-down handle and fitted lid.
- Microwave-proof plastic trivet or grid (to raise dishes from bottom of cooker (for casseroles and baking); especially useful for non-turntable microwaves.
- Clear, toughened glass or microwave-proof plastic ring dish: 23cm/9in and 25cm/10in diameters. This is the ideal shape for microwave cooking.
- Glazed pottery kugelhof ring mould: 23cm/9in and 25cm/10in diameters.

RIGHT: A selection of microwave cooking utensils, including a trivet, an oval steamer with transparent lid, a measuring jug, a muffin tray, a pasta cooker/drainer, a ring dish and a meat roaster. The metal casserole holder is purely for serving and should not be used in a microwave oven.

Kebabs or sausages on non-metal skewers (such as bamboo sticks) cook most evenly when they are well spaced around the outside edge of the dish.

Flipping meat over to an unused and therefore hotter part of the preheated browning dish speeds up cooking and streamlines browning.

- Toughened glass casserole.
- Six-hole, microwave-proof plastic bun/muffin tray.
- 'Baker-Lina' brand PTFE-coated (Teflon) non-stick cloth, 33×60cm/13×24in.
- Microwave-safe clingfilm.
- Microwave-proof plastic saucepan (with handle and pouring lip) with bent-handled ladle (to fit); plus stirrer and fish slice of same material.

Materials to avoid

Melamine and polystyrene plastics, recycled paper, lead crystal or glass, or china repaired with glue. Never use metal.

Covers & covering

- Always buy plastic film which specifies 'for microwave use', and never any other kind.
- Covering foods speeds up cooking. Steam build-up raises pressure and temperature. Pierce covering in a few places to prevent undue steam build-up.
- Remove clingfilm carefully, edge farthest away from your face first.
- Lids and the containers themselves can become hot with transferred heat. Use oven gloves.
- Twist paper, leaves, etc. underneath and fasten with natural fibre string, satay sticks, cocktail sticks.
- If food is to be stirred, checked or turned, cover with a lid or a plate (easy to remove).
- Greaseproof and baking parchment prevent spatter and keep some steam in, but do not seal airtight.
- Kitchen paper (not recycled) lets steam escape and, on cooker floor, absorbs moisture.

Using browning dishes

- Browning dishes have heat-absorbing material in their bases that can heat them to 220–280°C. They have small feet or ridges to prevent the super-heated base from touching the microwave. Check for these feet or ridges when buying one.
- Preheat according to the manufacturer's instructions or the timing given in specific recipes: 5 minutes (hot) to 8 minutes (extremely hot) is the normal range.
- When adding food, do not remove the dish from the microwave if possible. Always remember to wear oven gloves.
- After quickly adding the food to be browned (especially steaks, chicken breasts etc), press down on the food to increase contact with the heated dish, using tongs or a fish slice. When you are ready to turn the food over, remember to flip it on to an unused part of the dish – which is therefore hotter and more effective.
- 'Naturally golden' tasty substances such as soy sauce, hoisin sauce, plum sauce, chilli sauces, Barbados sugar, dark honey, balsamic vinegar, ground spices, curry paste, malt extract or apple concentrate may be used to enhance both colour and tastes; however, flavours must integrate. Follow recipe instructions.

RIGHT: A selection of microwave-safe wrappings and bindings, including kitchen paper, special microwave plastic film, baking parchment, non-stick cloth, greaseproof paper, roasting bags and ties, and banana, vine and sweetcorn leaves.

When sealing oven bags with non-metal ties, leave a finger-sized hole to prevent pressure build-up and splitting.

Loosely wrap french bread with kitchen paper to absorb moisture and prevent sogginess.

DIETING FOR LIFE

Eating well depends on a positive state of mind and a daily devotion to selecting the best foods. It should not be a question of short-term targets. Feeling good about yourself is important. Few people like being overweight and it's neither fashionable nor convenient. In Britain 30–35 per cent of adults are overweight – more than just a bit plump. According to some surveys, 8–12 per cent of us are obese – a real excess of accumulated body fat that can become a serious health hazard.

Show a slimming diet plan to most people and they will apologize, yawn, produce a reasoned argument why it doesn't apply to them and then make a rapid exit. If you are tired of trick diets, liquid diets, starvation regimes, and tedious but still expensive 'ready-meal' products, stuffed with unnecessary additives, this eating plan will cheer you up. It involves carefully chosen and cooked food, seasoned and served with style but capable of infinite variation.

A SLIM CHANCE: THE DIET CON TRICK

Nutrients matter, calories count. Food is the body's fuel. To believe you will become wafer-thin by buying and eating a special 'diet food' or pill or by following some crackpot 'combining' regime with sweeping generalizations about what food matches what, lacks common sense and reason. What we must eat is a wide range of mineral- and vitamin-high foods, ideally also low in calories, and learn to eat less of them. Snack mainly on fruits, vegetables, and wholegrain foods; replace over-refined products with less processed ones; give up (or reduce) super-sweet items and high-fat foods and instead eat more starchy, slowly absorbed, high-fibre foods. We must also learn to stop treating food as good or bad, and relax. Take enjoyable exercise to stay fit, and live a full life that extends beyond the kitchen.

Microwave cooking can really help. Lower-fat, lower-sugar, lower-salt but high-fibre foods, microwave-cooked, can taste surprisingly delicious. More of the original nutrients stay put (less cooking water, more efficient heating, less oxidation and damage to tissues). Because of its ease and simplicity microwave cooking sets you free to create more adventurous extras to make meals go with a bang. It should also let you relax and enjoy yourself so that healthy eating becomes the norm and a pleasure.

Being overweight and having a poor pattern of eating can be linked to various diet-related difficulties. High blood pressure, diabetes, high blood cholesterol are all factors increasing the risk of coronary heart disease (CHD). Shortage of vitamins A, C, E and beta carotene (an anti-oxidant) is thought to lead to premature ageing, cell damage and a predisposition to cancer. Excess weight also causes osteoarthritis, back complaints and other fitness problems.

Knowing this, it makes good sense to stay at least moderately trim. Since being overweight is definitely caused by too many calories (an imbalance between energy intake and output – basic metabolism plus activity) the answer lies in our diet and the amount of exercise we take. To eat less but better, and exercise more, we should use all the facilities at our disposal. The microwave is one of these.

DIET IS THE KEY

The answer is to select nutrient-packed foods of high quality and excellent, interesting flavour. Choose foods lower in fat (especially saturated fat) and low in added sugar, without excessive salt or chemical additives. If the main food groups are properly represented, then the vitamins, minerals and trace elements tend to take care of themselves.

The traditional protein-rich group of dairy food, fish, meat, eggs is no longer considered essential. Protein is vital but enough is present in cereals, leafy and starchy vegetables, pulses and nuts. This mixture also ensures that protein quality is not a problem.

Eat more soluble and insoluble dietary fibre. The range is between 12–24 grams a day (currently most of us barely eat 12 grams a day).

Young children need lots of energy so don't overdo their dietary fibre. This could make it difficult for them to get the calories and nutrients they need each day because they'd feel too 'full'. (Adults on a weight-loss diet appreciate that same full feeling, however.)

Examples of dietary fibre levels: 125g/4oz baked beans contains 4.1 grams of fibre; a 25g/1oz helping of high-fibre bran cereal has about 7.4 grams; 2 slices of wholewheat bread or toast would give you another 4.6 grams. The water-soluble fibre compounds help reduce blood cholesterol levels naturally. This is yet another reason why fresh fruit, vegetables and wholegrain foods are so valuable.

ARE YOU OVERWEIGHT?

The British government publication *Health of the Nation* claims that 8 per cent of adult men and 12 per cent of adult women are obese. How do they work it out? They use a calculation that gives the 'Body Mass Index' (BMI). This is how it works: take your height in metres and square it (multiply it by itself); divide your weight in kilograms by this number. The result is your index number. *For example:* you are 1.66 metres/5ft 6in tall. Square this and you get 2.76. Your weight is 57.3kg/9 stone. Divide the weight by the square of the height and your BMI is 21.2.

- If your BMI is less than 20 you are underweight.
- If your BMI is between 20 and 25 you are OK.
- If your BMI is between 25 and 30 you should lose weight.
- If your BMI is over 30 you are obese. You must start losing weight now.

Calories do count

A kilocalorie (usually called a calorie or written kcal) is the amount of energy needed to raise the temperature of 1 kilogram of water from 15°C to 16°C. Kilojoules are the metric version and 1 kilojoule is roughly ¼ of a kilocalorie. Most of us find it easier to think in calories.

1 gram of carbohydrate gives	4 kcals
1 gram of protein gives	4 kcals
1 gram of fat gives	9 kcals
1 gram of alcohol gives	7 kcals

It is easy to see from these figures that fat is more than twice as calorific (fattening) as carbohydrates or proteins. Watch out for the hidden fat in animal products – choose wisely.

Losing weight: activity & calorie use

Every 450g/1lb of fat in your body represents 3500 calories. If you normally need 1900 calories a day to stay at the same weight and only eat 1200 calories, you will be short of 4900 calories a week. This is the equivalent of a little less than 675g/1½ lb of fat. As there is a water loss associated with fat loss this means you should lose about 900g/2lb a week, a realistic aim.

Physical work and exercise burn up calories but not as much as some people think. The activities listed here give you some idea of how exercise assists in a weight-loss diet. These figures are approximate: the harder you work at it the more calories you use. Age, weight, height and sex help determine our calorie needs, along with our individual metabolic rate. Strenuous exercise as opposed to a sedentary life greatly affects our requirements, as do pregnancy and breast-feeding. Because men and women have different body densities, their calorie needs vary.

CALORIE USE PER HOUR		
ACTIVITY	WEIGHT	CALORIES
Running or jogging	50k/110lb	375
(at 8kmph/5mph)	68k/150lb	425
Cycling	50k/110lb	150–400
	68k/150lb	200–550
Low-impact aerobics	50k/110lb	200
	68k/150lb	275
Swimming	50k/110lb	475
(breaststroke)	68k/150lb	700
Tennis & squash	50k/110lb	400–600
	68k/150lb	550–850

WEIGHT-LOSS & STAY-SLIM EATING HINTS

- Don't overload your plate. A smaller plate helps resolve.
- Be last to be served, last to finish. Don't rush.
- Say no to seconds (except for growing children and the very active).
- Drink spring water in preference to alcohol, sugary drinks, 'diet' drinks or even fruit juices. Water is calorie free and an essential.
- Increase your intake of whole raw fresh fruits and vegetables. It takes longer to eat an orange from scratch than swallow a glass of juice. Since some basic nutrients are damaged or lost by processing, the original food is the better choice.
- Put salad on your side plate rather than too much white bread and lots of butter.
- Choose fresh fruits (or low-sugar cooked fruits) and maybe a little cheese for dessert rather than sugary or high-fat desserts.
- Enjoy low-fat forms of dairy products. Virtually-no-fat fromage frais is much lower in fat than any kind of cream and many yogurts, but high in protein, calcium and vitamins.
- Soft cheeses made from fat-free curds still taste excellent for eating and cooking. Some classic cheeses are low-fat too, some are not. Enjoy them all but in appropriate amounts.
- Select a high-fibre, low-salt and -sugar breakfast cereal if possible, or at least one sweetened naturally using dried fruits (intrinsic sugars). Add nuts, seeds and dried fruits to boring but virtuous high-bran cereals, or better still make your own 'customized' muesli.

- Use garlic, herbs, spices, home-made condiments as tasty extras, not endless salt and butter.
- Don't forget about porridge. Pinhead or fine or medium oatmeal are better choices (less processed) than rolled oats. They take a little longer to cook.
- Wheatgerm, oatbran or wheatbran can all be added to breakfast cereals. Store them, once opened, in a cool dark place (preferably a fridge or freezer). Use a pot or jar that can go to the table.
- Enjoy poultry, game and seafood (especially oily fish because it is so good for heart health) and fat-trimmed, well-reared meat of all types. Delicious red meat contains valuable nutrients, especially iron, which is easily absorbed.
- Cook protein foods carefully without much added fat and eat small servings with vegetables, rice or pasta.
- Select fruit, vegetables or lean fishy snacks (canned fish in brine are useful) rather than pastries and deep-fried and heavily salted snacks such as crisps. Rich dips containing cream, full-fat cheeses or mayonnaise are very calorific.
- Beans, peas, lentils, rice, pasta, potatoes, white fish, and most fruits and vegetables contain little or no fat. These are pivotal.

NOTE: Look after the fats, alcohols and sugars and the calories will look after themselves. Keep up some regular exercise and the weight will stay off. Enjoy breaking these rules now and then. Being confident that you can repair the damage is important. An 'after-binge' diet for 2 days or so will help restore the balance, along with some extra exercise.

ACCEPTABLE WEIGHTS FOR MEN AND WOMEN							
MEN				**WOMEN**			
HEIGHT (barefoot)		WEIGHT (without clothes)		HEIGHT (barefoot)		WEIGHT (without clothes)	
ft in	cm	lb	kg	ft in	cm	lb	kg
5.5	165	121–152	55–69	5.0	152	96–125	44–57
5.6	168	124–156	56–71	5.1	155	99–128	45–58
5.7	170	128–161	58–73	5.2	157	102–131	46–59
5.8	173	132–166	60–75	5.3	160	105–134	48–61
5.9	175	136–170	62–77	5.4	162	108–138	49–62
5.10	178	140–174	64–79	5 5	165	111–142	51–65
5.11	180	144–179	65–80	5.6	168	114–146	52–66
6.0	183	148–184	67–83	5.7	170	118–150	53–67
6.1	185	152–189	69–86	5.8	173	122–154	55–69
6.2	188	156–194	71–88	5.9	175	126–158	58–72
6.3	191	160–199	73–90	5.10	178	130–163	59–74

STEPS TO HEALTHIER FOOD CHOICES; BETTER COOKING; EFFECTIVE DIET PLANS

- Try one new fruit or vegetable each week. Keep your food choices wide and seasonal.
- Select lean cuts of meat and cook them by lean methods. Trim off visible fat, or in the case of poultry, don't eat the skin.
- Butter contains 66 per cent saturated fats. Use it sparingly if – as I do – you prefer its taste to margarine, which has 23 per cent saturated fat. Otherwise, try to substitute olive oil for butter where possible.
- Use little jam; or use a reduced-sugar product or pure fruit spread instead.
- Get smart about other fats: change from full-fat to semi-skimmed milk, full-fat yogurt to live, low-fat types. Use fromage frais instead of cream. Cut down (or cut out) pastries (especially fried ones), fried breakfasts, fried savoury snacks altogether.
- Lick your sugar habit: quarter the number of times you eat cakes, biscuits, confectionery, candy bars, icecream, high-fat sugary foods.
- Choose fruit for pudding. Buy fruits canned or bottled in juice (not syrup).
- Vegetables and fish, canned or bottled in stock or brine, are less calorific than in oil. Drain first.
- Get used to sliced ginger, mint sprigs, lemon or lime slices and cinnamon sticks or cloves to flavour tea or coffee, rather than sugar or cream.
- If you must add salt, use only a pinch of seasalt flakes. Because you can feel and see them you tend to use less. They contain other minerals and delicious sea flavours as well.
- Pasta, whether fresh or dry (especially thin, fine varieties) cooks well in the microwave (though no faster) and reheats beautifully too. Choose from Italian, Chinese and Japanese; wheat, rice and buckwheat types – be adventurous. Serve good pasta very simply: just a dollop of natural yogurt or fromage frais, some black pepper, chopped herbs and crushed garlic will taste sensational. Or use any salsa, sauce, dip, spread or coulis from this book. Light shavings of block Parmesan can be bliss.
- Potatoes cook like a dream in a microwave. Keep them uncut (or minimally cut), with skins on. Bake them, 'wedge-cook' them, 'bag-cook' them, steam them or make square chips. Potatoes make superb tasty snacks or main dishes.

- Eat green vegetables daily, especially dark green, leafy types, and all from the brassica family.
- Fruits make sensational purées and sauces. With spicy dressings (cooked or raw, skins on whenever possible) they're superb as salads. Smoked and cured fish, meats, poultry and game suit fresh fruit accompaniments and pastes (such as quince 'membrillo'). Apricots in dried sheet form (as amardine) and dried fruits are useful but rather calorific.
- Fresh berry fruits, mashed and folded into low-fat natural yogurt, rice or muesli, are effortless and low in calories. Underripe bananas make instant snacks.
- Enjoy cooking and flavouring foods with good alcohol in small amounts: dark rum, brandy, whisky and gin, dry sherry, vermouth and eau-de-vie. Drink distinctive wine in moderation. It is healthy for the heart and gives great pleasure. Just remember to stick to your doctor's recommended weekly alcohol unit allowance.
- A convivial 'balanced meal' at least once a day is a good idea. Eating habits can get out of order and, after all, eating is a social activity.
- Several vegetables along with a protein food (fish, game, eggs, cheese, pulses, or meat) add up to a good meal. End with fresh fruit.
- If you are a lacto-vegetarian, eat wholegrain cereals rather than refined ones each day, at least one piece of fruit, a salad and/or a coloured vegetable. One serving of cheese, beans, nuts or eggs per day plus 300ml/½ pint of milk or soy milk in the same meal balance amino acids. Beer, chips, chocolate bars and nuts do not make a healthy vegetarian diet!
- Any regime that limits what can be eaten with what ('combining' systems, for example) is likely to be unhelpful, and no guarantee of well-being or weight loss either. We need a wide range of foods, of nutrients eaten together. Thirteen major vitamins and 15 minerals are essential. We are omnivores whose digestive processes are subtle and complex. For example: vitamin C (ascorbic acid), say from 2 green and one starchy root vegetable, could help the iron from liver, kidney, steak, sardines or a wholegrain dish to be properly absorbed and used by the body. Vitamin C is also an anti-oxidant, helping rid the body of damaging free radicals.
- Manufactured snack foods can be fun but they tend to be sugar, salt and fat high or full of unnecessary additives. Real foods taste better.

REVELATIONS IN FOOD HEALTH & NUTRITION

A, C, E & beta carotene

Some micro-nutrients (nutrients found in tiny amounts in our food) are not only capable of preventing deficiency diseases but seem actively helpful in other newly important areas. One particular group – vitamins A, C, E and beta carotene (along with the mineral selenium) – have a powerful effect as naturally occurring anti-oxidants. These seem to protect the body from the harmful effects of free radicals, which are unstable, highly reactive breakdown products that form in the body in response to alcohol, exhaust fumes, cigarette smoke and as a by-product of our normal metabolism. Free radicals can cause havoc: they can alter the LDL (low-density lipoproteins – bad cholesterol in the bloodstream) and make them more likely to build up and clog the arteries, causing heart disease. Anti-oxidants help to neutralize these free radicals.

'Eat your greens' (plus your carrots, tomatoes and apricots) seems to make better sense than ever, although it never really went out of fashion.

Folic acid

Folic acid, a member of the vitamin B group, is now thought very important, especially for pregnant women during the first 12 weeks. Green vegetables, breakfast cereals and breads fortified with folic acid, as well as liver and kidney (well cooked), are important sources.

Garlic

Allicin, the active ingredient found in garlic, as well as being anti-bacterial, seems to reduce blood cholesterol considerably and is believed to be another anti-oxidant. Fresh garlic (not the processed type or pills) keeps all its allicin intact. The less contact with metal the better, so chop or crush it quickly and use it generously.

Fish oils

All oily fish, such as mackerel, salmon, herrings, sardines and sprats, contain Omega-3 fatty acids which are thought to help maintain heart health.

Zinc

Found in oysters, liver and wholemeal bread, zinc helps create and utilize energy uptake, helped by the presence of protein (meat, dairy products, eggs). So for those who have been rather too dismissive of meat, it seems time to make a reappraisal, especially if you like your wine (zinc availability is decreased by alcohol consumption).

DAILY USE OF THE DIETS

The two, week-long diets given here are just an example of the kind of diet you can construct for yourself. Don't follow them rigidly week after week! Use the calorie-counted recipes and ideas here to construct your own. You should have a wide and varying choice of foods appropriate to your lifestyle, your preferences and the season.

I have calculated the diets for women and teenage girls, so add on extras for men, teenage boys and the very active. The easiest way to make up the calorie differences is to allow yourself extra helpings. Many dishes serve 6 or even 8. This allows extras for some people or for extra food to be eaten cold, the next day, in other ways. For example, cold, leftover Singapore Chicken in its broth becomes jellied. It is delicious used in sandwiches or with leafy greens as salad. Alternatively, allow yourself healthy extras to make up the 300–600 calorie difference (depending on which diet you are using). Award yourself an extra apple, kiwi fruit and banana or some more muesli with some skimmed milk, another jacket potato, more pasta, a peanut butter wholewheat sandwich, a piece of polenta pizza or some nachos.

If you don't need to lose weight but just want to eat an optimum diet, follow the EVERYDAY HIGH-HEALTH DIET, adding one or two extra high-quality foods of choice. Stop when you see any consistent weight gain. Build in an extra 200-calorie jump every two days. Go back to the level just before the one at which you started to gain weight and you will have found the calorie level that suits your body and lifestyle.

Allow hunger to control calorie levels too. If you feel comfortable eating a little below the given levels then do so. But if you start to feel consistently hungry (unlikely with slow carbohydrate release) while on the given calorie levels, then slightly increase your bulky, fibre-high foods – the low-calorie ones, especially bran-boosted cereals and leafy salads. Substitute these for, say, a sugar- or fat-containing 'flavour' food like the Amardine Apricot Velvet Drink or 2tbsp vinaigrette. Have a big, stylish, mixed green herby salad instead with fromage frais (not vinaigrette) dressing to compensate.

Another self-help solution is to step-up your exercise levels and increase the 'feel-good' hormones which make you stay positive and in control. Three brisk 30-minute sessions per week of an aerobic activity you enjoy helps avoid losing muscle as well as fat: in losing weight the aim is to lose the fat only. Beware: crash diets cause muscle loss too.

FOOD SELECTION, DIET & HEALTH

The Government's recommendations are:
- Ideally 15 per cent of our energy (calories) should come from PROTEIN; say 85g/3oz per day give 300 calories. (350g/12oz of lean beef contain about 85g/3oz of protein – much of the weight is water and other nutrients.)
- At least 50 per cent of calories should come from CARBOHYDRATES (especially starchy ones); say 250g/9oz per day give 1000 calories. (Once again, foods are pure carbohydrate.)
- Up to 30 per cent of calories may come from FATS and OILS, and of these 20 per cent should be mono-unsaturated ones (olive oil etc) and only 10 per cent saturated (hard animal fats and hydrogenated oils etc). 67g/2½ oz per day give 600 calories worth.

All these add up to 1900 calories a day.

The WEIGHT-LOSS DIET is based on about 1200 calories a day for an average-sized woman or teenage girl. For a moderately active man I have allowed 1500 calories a day plus up to 200 extra calories for the more active and teenage boys.

The EVERYDAY HIGH-HEALTH DIET allows for 1900 calories for an average woman or teenage girl, and up to 2500 calories a day for a man or teenage boy.

The AFTER-BINGE CLEAR-OUT PLAN allows about 1500 calories but is helpful for vitality and restoring

balance after excesses, before returning to a 1200 calorie a day diet. It consists of no animal products, lots of fruits, vegetables, grains, nuts and seeds and no coffee or tea.

The ENTERTAINING MENUS show how to combine the recipes in this book for delicious, well-balanced celebration food. They range from a picnic for eight to a romantic meal for two. When entertaining and dieting, it helps to have spring water, good bread, raw fruit and salad. Remember too to mix spicy and bland; contrast hot, warm, and cold; rough against smooth; colourful with plain. All these will create interest and prevent boredom. Try not to repeat more than one creamy food or baby-smooth texture. Keep colours truthful and plates unfussy.

CONVERSION TABLE			
This conversion is based on 4.2 kJ to 1 kcal			
K/CAL	K/JOULE	K/JOULE	K/CAL
1	4	1	0
5	21	5	1
10	42	10	2
20	84	20	5
30	126	30	7
40	168	40	10
50	210	50	12
60	252	60	14
70	294	70	17
80	336	80	19
90	378	90	21
100	420	100	24
200	840	200	48
300	1260	300	71
400	1680	400	95
500	2100	500	119
1000	4200	1000	238
1500	6300	2000	476
2000	8400	3000	714
2500	10500	4000	952
3000	12600	5000	1190
3500	14700	6000	1429

Weight-loss Diet

THIS SEVEN-DAY DIET IS BASED ON A DAILY INTAKE OF
1200 CALORIES FOR AN AVERAGE WOMAN. MEN AND TEENAGERS
ARE ALLOWED 1500 CALORIES A DAY

MONDAY

Breakfast:

Instant porridge in a plate ★
Tea, 4tbsp skimmed milk

Mid-morning:

*Iced mineral water,
slice lime*

Lunch:

*Polenta pizza
with sun-dried
tomatoes* ★
2 celery sticks
1 × 85g/3oz carrot
6 radishes

Mid-afternoon:

*1 pear or
small banana*

Dinner:

2 low-fat poppadums ★
Chicken mishmish ★
Green beans with garlic ★
*Baby potatoes with wine
& mint* ★
*125g/4oz sliced, cinnamon-
dusted strawberries*
1 glass dry white wine
Black coffee

• ABOUT 1199 CALORIES •

TUESDAY

Breakfast:

¹/₂ pink grapefruit
1 slice wholewheat toast
Smoked mackerel toast topper ★
Tisane or black coffee

Mid-morning:

Tea, 4tbsp skimmed milk

Lunch:

Iced mineral water, slice lemon
¹/₂ baked potato with chive topping

Mid-afternoon:

Trinidadian rosella drink on ice ★

Dinner:

Capsicum soup Ortiz, hot or iced ★
Blanquette de veau ★
Wild rice & leek greens ★
1 tomato, sliced
*50g/2oz sliced cucumber
with mint*
1 glass dry white wine
Black coffee

• ABOUT 1252 CALORIES •

★ *Asterisks indicate recipes included
in the book.*

WEDNESDAY

Breakfast:

Instant scrambled egg ★
Wholewheat toast
¹/₂ orange, cut in two
Hot chocolate drink ★

Mid-morning:

Tea with mint sprig or black coffee
Iced mineral water, slice lemon

Lunch:

Two-minute smoked salmon dip ★
2 rye crispbreads
1 small tomato
¹/₂ corn on the cob au naturel ★
1tbsp cheat's lower-fat dressing ★

Mid-afternoon:

Rosehip tea or tisane

Dinner:

¹/₂ hot wholemeal pitta
Mushrooms in wine ★
Fish in paper ★
Carrots au naturel ★
Cauli florets in spiced dressing ★
Mangetouts au naturel ★
Mango with lime ★
Black coffee

• ABOUT 1188 CALORIES •

THURSDAY

Breakfast:
Hot spiced apple & yogurt ★
2tsp wheatgerm
1 wholewheat crispbread
1tsp butter
Tisane or black coffee

Mid-morning:
Tofu malt shake ★

Lunch:
Mint & barley salad ★
*50g/2oz mixed green salad,
squeeze of lemon juice*
1 fig
Iced mineral water

Mid-afternoon:
Peppermint & lemon honey tea ★

Dinner:
Trimpork bolognese ★
Aubergine au naturel ★
Asparagus au naturel ★
Berry parfait icecream ★
1 spice and nut wafer biscuit
Black coffee, tea or tisane

• ABOUT 1178 CALORIES •

FRIDAY

Breakfast:
Bircher muesli ★
6tbsp buttermilk
Lemon tea

Mid-morning:
Iced mineral water
Instant hot orange pressé ★

Lunch:
Green velvet soup, hot or cold ★
Salmon kebabs with salsa ★
1 sesame crispbread

Mid-afternoon:
*Lemon barley water (2tsp with water
and ice)* ★

Dinner:
Pepper & goat's cheese paste ★
Chicory leaves
Red rice with vegetables ★
25g/1oz spinach
25g/1oz bok choy
25g/1oz rocket
1tbsp classic vinaigrette ★
1/2 pear, sliced
2tbsp virtually-no-fat fromage frais
Coffee, tea or tisane

• ABOUT 1202 CALORIES •

SATURDAY

Breakfast:
Perfect poached egg ★
1 wholewheat muffin, toasted
1tsp butter
1tsp reduced-sugar blackcurrant jam

Mid-morning:
*Elderflower syrup, mineral water
and ice*

Lunch:
Home-style burgers ★
125g/4oz fresh cherries

Mid-afternoon:
Tea with lemon or lime

Dinner:
Instant hot orange pressé ★
Radishes on ice ★
*Poultry brochettes with prunes
& calvados* ★
6 cos lettuce leaves
85g/3oz fresh raspberries
2tbsp virtually-no-fat fromage frais
Coffee, tea or tisane

• ABOUT 1230 CALORIES •

SUNDAY

Breakfast:
*Instant apple-orange purée
(half serving)* ★
2tbsp virtually-no-fat fromage frais
2tbsp high-fibre bran
1 wholewheat croissant
1tsp honey
Instant hot orange pressé ★

Mid-morning:
Lemon tea

Lunch:
*Celebration beef sirloin with black
olives (half serving)* ★
Microwave square 'chips' ★
Red cabbage, apple & juniper ★
Gin-lime jelly with grapes ★

Mid-afternoon:
Elderflower and lemon tea

Supper:
Vegetable pottage (half serving) ★
*Wilted salad with tamarillo
dressing* ★
Fig cartocchio ★

• ABOUT 1213 CALORIES •

EVERYDAY HIGH-HEALTH DIET

MAKE YOUR CALORIES COUNT! THIS SAMPLE DAILY DIET ALLOWS 1900 CALORIES FOR AN AVERAGE WOMAN, BUT MEN AND TEENAGERS ARE ALLOWED 2500 CALORIES, SO USE EXTRA SERVINGS OF FRUITS, VEGETABLES, NUTS, AND GRAIN AND PASTA PRODUCTS. BALANCE ANY EXCESS WITH 30 MINUTES' VIGOROUS EXERCISE.

MONDAY

Breakfast:
Low-fat citrus, nut & seed muesli *
100ml/4 fl oz buttermilk or skimmed milk
1 slice wholewheat toast
1tsp butter or very-low-fat spread
1tsp reduced-sugar jam

Mid-morning:
25g/1oz poppyseed popcorn *

Lunch:
100g/3½oz lettuce heart halves
1 × 50g/2oz carrot
Garlic & herb bread
1 small apple, plum, pear or orange
Chocolate drink *

Mid-afternoon:
Raspberry or blackcurrant tisane
1 rye crispbread
15g/½oz low-fat cheese

Dinner:
Almost-instant soup *
with 2 spring onions and
15g/½oz ginger
Pork chops adobo *
1 jacket potato, 100g/3½oz
Red cabbage, apple & juniper *
Bread pudding *
2tbsp virtually-no-fat fromage frais
Coffee or tisane

• ABOUT 1608 CALORIES •

TUESDAY

Breakfast:
Two-minute tomatoes on toast *
1 toasted muffin half
1tsp butter or very-low-fat spread
China tea with lemon

Mid-morning:
2 sesame crispbreads
1tbsp pesto with pistachios *
Iced mineral water

Lunch:
Open sandwiches on 2 slices
sourdough bread
6tbsp tandoori cheese dip *
Watercress and cucumber
Banana, melon or grapes

Mid-afternoon:
Lemon barley water, iced *

Dinner:
Smoked oyster risotto *
Raw spinach, red onion and
radish salad
1tsp classic vinaigrette *
Risogalo creamy rice *
Raspberries, blackberries or currants
Coffee or tisane

• ABOUT 1700 CALORIES •

WEDNESDAY

Breakfast:
Silken apple *
Cocotte egg *
2 slices toasted wholewheat bread
2tsp butter or very-low-fat spread
1tsp reduced-sugar marmalade
Coffee, tea or tisane

Mid-morning:
Instant hot orange pressé *

Lunch:
Spicy couscous* in mini pittas
2 tomatoes, sliced
1 mini mozzarella
Basil leaves
Fruit tea

Mid-afternoon:
Hot elderflower cordial
1 apple
15g/½oz low-fat Cheddar

Dinner:
Lemon grass chicken *
25g/1oz plain brown rice *
Brussels sprouts en papillote *
Fromage frais with 1 passionfruit
Hot chocolate drink *

• ABOUT 1942 CALORIES •

* Asterisks indicate recipes included
in the book.

THURSDAY

Breakfast:
Instant porridge in a plate ★
1 orange
Tofu malt shake ★

Mid-morning:
Tisane of choice

Lunch:
Chilli garlic prawns ★
Wild rice & leek greens ★
1 wholewheat roll
1tsp butter or very-low-fat spread

Mid-afternoon:
Rosehip tisane

Dinner:
Lamb kofta kebabs ★
Mint & barley salad ★
Red and green mixed leaf salad
*Fresh fruit salad: pear, melon,
banana and mango*
Black coffee, tea or tisane

• ABOUT 1625 CALORIES •

FRIDAY

Breakfast:
Risogalo creamy rice ★
Rhubarb au naturel ★
1 oat crispbread
1tsp butter
Tea, coffee or tisane

Mid-morning:
Nachos with melted cheese ★
Iced mineral water with mint

Lunch:
*Polenta pizza with sun-dried
tomatoes* ★
Jacket potato (plain)
1tbsp tamarillo relish ★
Little Gem lettuce
1 small apple

Mid-afternoon:
Scarlet strawberry cordial, iced ★

Dinner:
Harissa curd★ *and celery*
Smoked mackerel St Clement's ★
*50g/2oz red beans (canned) with
green pepper and red onion*
2tbsp classic vinaigrette ★
Raspberries with cinnamon
Coffee

• ABOUT 1493 CALORIES •

SATURDAY

Breakfast:
Bacon & tomato breakfast ★
2 toasted wholewheat muffins
1 tsp butter or very-low-fat spread
2tsp honey

Mid-morning:
Garlic & herb bread
1 low-alcohol lager

Lunch:
Tabbouleh on lettuce cups ★
Chicken Santa Cruz ★
*Mexican turtle beans with
coriander* ★
Peppers en papillote ★
Frozen kiwi instant sorbet ★

Mid-afternoon:
Instant hot lemon pressé ★

Dinner:
Trinidadian rosella drink ★
Courgette-topped fillets ★
Mangetouts au naturel ★
*Hot carrot shreds with orange
& coriander* ★
1tbsp classic vinaigrette ★
Coffee

• ABOUT 1943 CALORIES •

SUNDAY

Breakfast:
½ pink grapefruit
Perfect poached egg ★
2 slices wholewheat bread
2tsp butter
1tsp marmalade
Tea, coffee, tisane or milk

Mid-morning:
Red wine spritzer

Lunch:
Quail in red vermouth ★
Spiced potatoes with red lentils ★
Chicory, rocket and spinach salad
1tbsp classic vinaigrette ★
Pineapple with raw berry coulis ★

Mid-afternoon:
Juice special ★

Supper:
2 low-fat poppadums ★
Coriander guacamole ★
Cauli florets in spiced dressing ★
Kibbled wheat with herbs ★
Coffee

• ABOUT 2100 CALORIES •

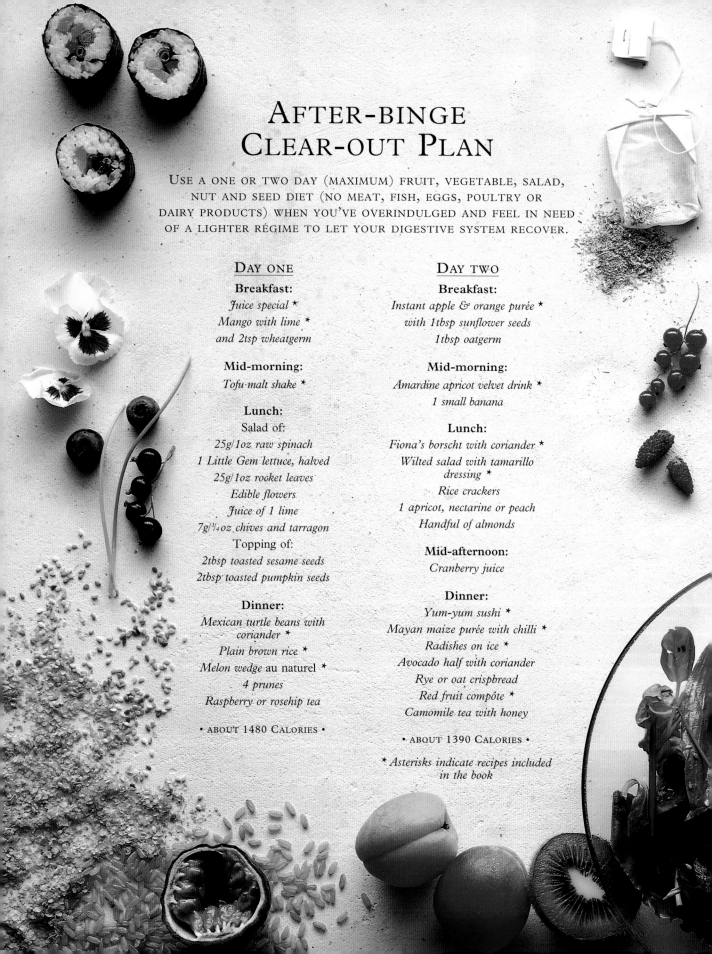

AFTER-BINGE
CLEAR-OUT PLAN

USE A ONE OR TWO DAY (MAXIMUM) FRUIT, VEGETABLE, SALAD, NUT AND SEED DIET (NO MEAT, FISH, EGGS, POULTRY OR DAIRY PRODUCTS) WHEN YOU'VE OVERINDULGED AND FEEL IN NEED OF A LIGHTER RÉGIME TO LET YOUR DIGESTIVE SYSTEM RECOVER.

DAY ONE

Breakfast:
Juice special ★
Mango with lime ★
and 2tsp wheatgerm

Mid-morning:
Tofu-malt shake ★

Lunch:
Salad of:
25g/1oz raw spinach
1 Little Gem lettuce, halved
25g/1oz rocket leaves
Edible flowers
Juice of 1 lime
7g/¼oz chives and tarragon
Topping of:
2tbsp toasted sesame seeds
2tbsp toasted pumpkin seeds

Dinner:
Mexican turtle beans with coriander ★
Plain brown rice ★
Melon wedge au naturel ★
4 prunes
Raspberry or rosehip tea

• ABOUT 1480 CALORIES •

DAY TWO

Breakfast:
Instant apple & orange purée ★
with 1tbsp sunflower seeds
1tbsp oatgerm

Mid-morning:
Amardine apricot velvet drink ★
1 small banana

Lunch:
Fiona's borscht with coriander ★
Wilted salad with tamarillo dressing ★
Rice crackers
1 apricot, nectarine or peach
Handful of almonds

Mid-afternoon:
Cranberry juice

Dinner:
Yum-yum sushi ★
Mayan maize purée with chilli ★
Radishes on ice ★
Avocado half with coriander
Rye or oat crispbread
Red fruit compôte ★
Camomile tea with honey

• ABOUT 1390 CALORIES •

★ *Asterisks indicate recipes included in the book*

ENTERTAINING MENUS

ENTERTAINING NEED NOT MEAN CREAMY, BUTTERY SAUCES
AND TOO-RICH PUDDINGS. MAXIMIZE FRUIT, VEGETABLE, PASTA AND
GRAIN DISHES FOR   PLEASURABLE EATING.

SUMMER PICNIC LUNCH

FOR 8

(Cold foods to make ahead)

Lemon barley water *
with ice and mineral water

Scarlet strawberry cordial *
with ice and sparkling white wine

*Bagel open sandwiches with
harissa curd* *

American pickles *
and celery

Tabbouleh on lettuce cups *
with cherry tomatoes

Lamb kofta kebabs *

Bille's pickled herrings *

Baby potatoes with wine & mint *

Aubergines au naturel *

*Cherries, berries, peach and melon
slices in Pineau des Charentes*

*Iced coffee or
apple and lemon 'tea'*

ROMANTIC MEAL
FOR LOVERS

FOR 2

Radishes on ice *
with Hong Kong firecracker sauce *

Chilli garlic prawns *

Asparagus au naturel *

Crusty French bread

Figs cartoccio *

Tisane

* Asterisks indicate recipes included
in the book.

CELEBRATION SUPPER
FOR FRIENDS

FOR 4

Pepper and goat's cheese paste *
sourdough bread

*Poultry brochettes with prunes
& calvados* *

Kibbled wheat with herbs *

*Watercress, avocado and red onion
salad with classic vinaigrette* *

Gin-lime jelly with grapes *

Coffee or tea

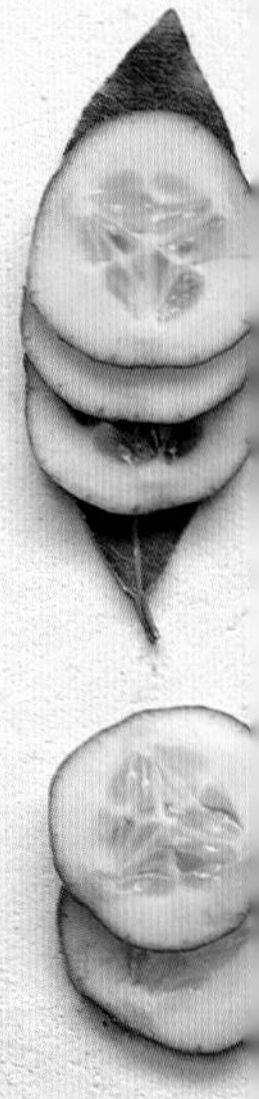

BUDGET MEAL

FOR 4

Hummus-kipper pâté *
with celery

Hot pitta breads

One-dish macaroni cheese *
with sliced tomatoes

Green beans with garlic *

Instant apple-orange purée *
with iced yogurt

Coffee

IMPROMPTU SUPPER PARTY

FOR 6

Spicy low-fat poppadums ★
with mango chutney

Butterfly pasta, bresaola & peas ★
with sliced tomatoes

Sliced cucumber with mint

Ciabatta

Raw berry coulis ★
with fromage frais and crisp wafers

Coffee

BUSINESS LUNCH

FOR 4

Coriander guacamole ★
with chicory spears

Smoked oyster risotto ★

Frozen kiwi instant sorbet ★

Coffee

BIRTHDAY DINNER

FOR 6

Two-minute smoked salmon dip ★
with lettuce

Magic rack of lamb ★

or Celebration beef sirloin with
black olives ★

Red onions au naturel ★

Mayan maize purée with chilli ★

Berry parfait icecream ★
with virtually-no-fat fromage frais

Coffee

THE LIBERATED
LARDER

Select the best, most distinctive ingredients you can afford. Cook them appropriately (often this means as little as possible) to make them taste delicious. Present the dishes simply with the confidence of pleasures ahead. . . This is enlightened eating and sums up my cooking philosophy.

The best food tastes of itself. Proper regard for each food doesn't mean, however, that you can't mix and match a little. Ethnic, 'organic' or speciality foods now jostle for space on many of our superstore shelves, making our kitchens cross-cultural playgrounds.

Eclectic blends of raw materials, flavours, techniques and ideas can make us into properly ambitious eaters, and aware of the true potential of each food. Various things have helped set us free. The most radical of these is the microwave. But liberated cooks also need a blender, a food processor, a bamboo steamer, a juicer, coffee grinder and wok to make short work of their cooking. Pasta machines and icecream makers can revolutionize your methods and your eating too, but these are luxuries. The spectrum of exciting dishes constantly expands. Superfast recipes and difficult cooking procedures were once only the domain of chefs, experts and specialist producers. Now we can expect success with many of these at home, using hi-tech appliances such as the microwave to reduce cooking processes to their purest, simplest state.

Spectacular advances in growing, harvesting, preparing, packaging and transporting many once-perishable or highly seasonal food items in this jet age, now mean that we can 'steal from the world's cuisines' with ease. We can also widen and enrich our daily diets. Variety is the boredom beater par excellence, both in produce and in cooking procedure.

Sauvignon Blanc from New Zealand, cherries from Chile, black beans from Bolivia, Sicilian vine-ripened tomatoes, crispbreads from Finland, blue corn chips from New Mexico: these have become new items possible for everyday use. Even so, don't forget the joys of locally produced goods at peak season. A fresh-picked raspberry or damson or glistening silver oyster on its shell only hours from its estuary bed, taste sensational and are often real bargains.

A really liberated larder should provide, by its variety and good beginnings, the means to return home (tired, maybe late or both) having done minimal shopping and still be able to conjure up tasty, healthy meals without apparent effort, in minutes.

Eating a wide, sensible balanced diet based on seasonal good things will definitely help maintain well-being and fitness and help to fight the flab. Erratic eating, boring fuel stops or an unhealthy dependence on manufactured 'ready-meals' and snack foods all tend to happen most when there are not enough congenial starter materials in your store cupboard to back up your fresh food purchases, nor the means to cook them quickly, easily and well.

THE GREAT BUTTER DEBATE

The news is out: domestic microwave cooking is a step forward and all the snobbish food reactionaries were wrong. Many interesting dishes can be made superbly using the microwave. We have begun to cherish better, fresh, home-made food once again, rather than factory-assembled, so-called 'fast foods', many of which are frankly no longer naturally fresh. How can they be?

Over-processed foods that contain interminable lists of emulsifiers, stabilizers, bulking agents, colourants, anti-oxidants, synthetic flavourings, 'enrichment' agents (for 'mouth feel'), along with excessive salt, hydrogenated oils (with their nasty trans-fats), saturated fat 'shortenings' and sugar or synthetic sweeteners, are worrying. Many exist. 'Lo', 'Lite', and 'Reduced Calorie' are cynical names for (far too often) added air, added water. Why pay more for less? Make your own healthier, tastier versions. There is no such thing as a diet food, just decent diet.

Some recent products, the fat substitutes Simplesse, Nutrifat and non-digested 'altered state' fats such as Olestra, fool the tongue and the brain into thinking fat is present, but not the gut, leading to some pretty distasteful side effects... Can all this be good?

I love food-shopping diversity and adore eating out. But let's celebrate and remember real flavours, not laboratory-generated blends made using nature-identical flavourings, often in the exaggerated amounts that production-line foods need to boost their otherwise lacklustre flavours. Maybe it's because we are in danger of losing valued skills and forgetting the original shapes, textures, smells, colours and flavours of real food that I feel so passionately keen to restore pride in homely commonsense cooking, but using updated appliances to remove the drudgery and improve the food values.

In the following recipes the use of saturated fat has been deliberately minimized in the interests of good health. However, butter remains, since I adore its clean, honest flavour and loathe the synthetic butter substitutes. If you must make substitutions (butter contains 66% saturates, margarines 23%, after all), then go ahead.

Extra virgin olive oil is delicious and contains relatively few saturates and more mono-unsaturates – a heart helpful alternative. Since not all such substitutions work well, use your discretion remembering that these recipes are balanced to my taste.

ORGANIZING YOUR FOOD STORAGE

Though it is important, the store cupboard isn't your only larder. Think of your freezer as a frozen larder. In it you can store delicious foods that are rare, have a short season, don't keep well or require a lot of shopping effort. Some foods like root ginger can be used straight from frozen, grated straight into the dish. Coffee beans keep better very cold (the volatile oils do not become rancid or stale), yet can be ground from frozen.

Ethnic and specialist breads, sliced before freezing, can be taken out one piece at a time and warmed or toasted. Blue (raw) prawn tails on skewers, slivers of chicken breast, baby wild mushrooms, salmon cubes and free-flow berries are other examples of frozen foods that can jump easily from freezer to baking dish and enliven your eating no end.

Unexpected food gifts – a wild rabbit, some freshly picked greengages or windfall apples that cannot be used immediately – can also be frozen for later enjoyment.

If you think of the fridge as a chilled larder, you'll extend its function and your repertoire. Green herbs: loosely tie them, water-spray and put into a new plastic bag, then blow up the bag and its contents into an airtight 'bubble' and seal with a rubber band; they'll stay bouncy for a week. This is a real bonus. Young leafy green vegetables (spinach, lettuce, pak choy, rocket) can be treated the same way, though are most vitamin-packed when used within a few days.

Meat, fish and game should be loosely wrapped and kept quite separate from dairy foods which absorb smells and tastes. Cooked meats and fish should be kept above and quite separate from raw. Hard and medium cheeses are best paper wrapped or kept in greaseproof bags. Plastic bags if used must be loose-tied.

Current wisdom dictates keeping eggs separate from other food perishables because salmonella survive on the outside shell as well as the inside of the egg. It is essential therefore to keep eggs in their own compartment (in a cool larder or a fridge), and it always makes sense to buy them super-fresh from a reliable supplier.

RIGHT: Select high-quality limited-season foods that are in first-class condition for your freezer. Wrap them in appropriate freezer materials, then label and date them. Try to freeze in small quantities to ensure rapid turnover.

STORAGE GUIDELINES

Few householders could keep all of the following foods in the freezer, fridge or larder, but aim for a fair majority. The following suggestions include many of the products commonly used throughout this book. They will give your diet nutrient power, but equally importantly, will create interest and variety. They are especially valid for fast-cooked microwave dishes: their flavours are often the 'fast-release' type, or in an easily absorbed form.

FREEZER

Staples:
Berries, bread, chicken portions, ice cubes, peas, prawn tails (shell on), salmon steaks and fillets, stock (in ice cube trays) and meat essence from roasts.

Useful extras:
Banana leaf sheets and vine leaves (food wrappers), coffee beans (once gas-flush pack is opened), cured meats, fish (whole small red mullet, sardines, sprats, smoked fish), game, nuts (pecans, walnuts, hazelnuts, almonds), red meat and offal, seeds (sunflower, sesame, pumpkin, alfalfa), vodka (buffalo-grass type).

REFRIGERATOR

Many of these foodstuffs are not traditionally refrigerated. Deliberate, maximized use of the fridge certainly means greater vitamin retention and freshness of fruits, vegetables and herbs along with less deterioration and softening of tissues, colour and flavour losses. It extends their shelf life. For salads, milk and dairy products, and fresh foods, cool dark storage is essential. Many foods such as tomatoes, stonefruits and cheeses benefit from 'chambréing' (being left to stand at room temperature) before cooking and before eating.

Staples:
Apples, bacon, butter or low-fat spread, broccoli (or cauliflower or Romanesco type), cabbage and Brussels sprouts, carrots, cheese (Parmesan, Cheddar, low-fat soft spreadable cheese, blue cheese or goat's cheese), chillies, citrus fruit, fromage frais (virtually-no-fat type), ginger root, reduced-sugar jam and pure fruit spread, milk (skimmed, semi-skimmed; also soy milk), onions, parsley (in inflated, sealed plastic bags), peppers, potatoes, spring onions, spring water (sparkling and still), tomatoes (ideally vine-ripened on the stalk; also plum), white wine and/or cider, yogurt (natural with acidophilus and strained Greek).

Useful extras:
Amardine (dried apricot paste in sheet form), buttermilk (extremely low-fat dairy product), chives (in inflated, sealed bags), coconut (creamed or block form), coriander leaves (in inflated, sealed bags), lettuces, lemon grass (in inflated, sealed bags), mango, oatmeal (in sealed plastic bag for freshness), organic apple juice concentrate, pinenuts (in airtight container), sweet potatoes, yams or parsnips, tahini, tamarillos (vitamin-C high exotic fruits), tofu (in cartons), wheatgerm (in airtight container).

STORE CUPBOARD

Staples:
Cinnamon, cloves, cocoa powder, eggs, garlic (on a string or bunch), honey, nut oils (hazelnut, walnut), olive oil, peppercorns, polenta (precooked fine maize meal), poppadums (uncooked), rice, seed oils (dark sesame, grapeseed, sunflower), soy sauce, stock cubes, Thai Tom Yam cubes, tamarind stock cubes, salt (seasalt flakes), sugar (caster, dark muscovado, molasses), tea (traditional, peppermint, lemon verbena – beware artificially flavoured fruit teas, even those called 'nature identical'), vinegar, dried yeast, vanilla essence and pods.

Useful extras:
Alcohol (rum, eau de vie, brandy, gin, red wine, Pineau des Charentes), amchur (powdered mango), anchovy fillets and essence, beans and pulses, bulgur wheat, cardamom pods, dried chilli, coconut (chips, cream and milk), couscous (fine wheat-based pasta product), dried fruits, flours for thickening (*fécule* and arrowroot, rice starch), harissa (chilli-boosted paste), juniper berries, dried mushrooms, mustard and nigella seeds, nutmegs, olives, oysters (canned), pasta, pistachio nuts, plain rice noodles, dried rosella (roselle, sorrel, hibiscus), saffron, seaweed (Japanese nori sheets for sushi and wakame shreds for stock), sumac (deep red, sour seasoning powder), Szechuan pepper (also called anise pepper).

RIGHT: A fridge stocked with low-fat yogurts, fresh vegetables, fresh fish and organic meats will help you to cook delicious lean foods regularly. Eating is no longer guilt-ridden when you can turn your back on calorie-high convenience food.

BREAKFASTS:
RISE & SHINE

It has been said that we should 'breakfast like kings, lunch like princes and dine like paupers'. In terms of our metabolism and digestive systems this old saying makes good sense. The pressures of work and time and the demands of positive good health have done *away with the traditional daily English breakfast 'fry-up', now an occasional weekend indulgence. But a sustaining start to the day is still essential, particularly for those involved in energetic activities.*

Recent tests on the relationship of blood glucose levels and memory performance show that students who had eaten breakfast performed better than those who had not. Mid-morning chocolate bars and 'junk food' snacks lead to huge mood swings and depress hormone levels, so try to avoid them. After all, there are much nicer choices. Why not try a Tofu malt shake to banish the mid-morning blues?

My first chapter suggests some home-made 'fast food' breakfasts. Freshly cooked fruits or dried fruits in some home-made muesli, low-fat milk drinks and quick-cooked cereals are classics. Microwaved porridge, now known to be actively helpful for heart health as well as for easy digestion, is cooked and served from the same dish and is really heart-warming! So are the rice-based breakfasts. These are old-fashioned comfort foods, rejuvenated by the magic of speedy microwave cooking. There is a point in making them once again now that they are so easy and tasty.

As well as some simple egg dishes there is a fish paste to make ahead, pot and store in the fridge: true 'convenience food' for all-day use, but healthy too! Tomatoes on toast and lean bacon with tomatoes are possible mid-week morning starts. My new versions are speedy and low in saturates. A fragrant, hot drink of apple and lemon may even topple your outdated tea or coffee routine. Give it a try. Boredom defeats most diets – don't let it happen to yours!

It's also worth investing in an electric juicer to create all sorts of fresh juice cocktails. These look and taste sensational!

If all else fails, eat an apple en route to the train or slap some low-fat peanut butter on some toast: these are quality fast foods. Above all, forget outdated conventions. Breakfast as you like and make it a positive start to your day!

It is not for nothing that you see the sign 'Breakfast Served All Day' outside many thriving cafés. The combination of cereal and fruit, a protein food and toast or bread with a hot drink makes a sensible meal. There's every reason to eat breakfast-style meals at any time of the day or night. Please yourself.

LEFT: HOT SPICED APPLE & YOGURT; LOW-FAT CITRUS, NUT & SEED MUESLI

HOT SPICED APPLE & YOGURT

CALORIES PER SERVING: 59
SERVES: 4

VARIATIONS
1. Squeeze the juice of 1 orange over before adding the yogurt.
2. Substitute virtually-no-fat fromage frais for yogurt.
3. Add 1tsp flower-scented honey per serving, spooning it over the yogurt.
4. Add some chopped toasted almonds for extra crunch.

2 large crisp apples: Cox's, Gala, Royal Gala, Sturmer, Delicious, Braeburn or Fuji
¼ tsp ground allspice or nutmeg
8tbsp low-fat natural bio-yogurt

Wash the apples and remove the stalks. Grate the entire fruits including the core and skin, using the fine grater attachment of a

food processor or a coarse grater. Less vitamin C is lost this way.

Divide among 4 microwave-proof dishes. Dust each with some spice. Microwave, uncovered, on HIGH for 2 minutes. Spoon cold yogurt on top and enjoy the contrast of temperatures and textures as well as taste.

INSTANT APPLE-ORANGE PURÉE

THIS QUICKLY COOKED HOT FRUIT PURÉE CAN ALSO DOUBLE AS A SNACK FOOD
OR PUDDING. IT SETS ALMOST TO A JELLY WHEN CHILLED BECAUSE OF THE EFFECTIVENESS
OF THE MICROWAVE COOKING PROCESS, SO IT CAN BE KEPT IN THE FRIDGE FOR
AN IMPROMPTU SNACK.

CALORIES PER SERVING : 100
(WITHOUT FROMAGE FRAIS)
SERVES: 2

VARIATIONS
1. Chilled for 3–4 hours, it will set into a heart-healthy 'gel' because of natural gums and pectin. Delicious and intriguing.
2. Layer the cold purée alternately with low-fat natural bio-yogurt, in glasses. Serve as a party treat with amaretti biscuits, tuiles or crêpes dentelles.

225g/8oz apples: preferably 3 small Cox's Orange Pippins, stalks removed
150ml/¼ pint freshly squeezed orange juice
2tbsp virtually-no-fat fromage frais (optional)

Quarter each apple, then halve each piece to give 8 segments each. Arrange around the edge of a microwave-proof plate.

Microwave, uncovered, on HIGH for 3 minutes; halfway through, give the plate a half turn.

Immediately blend or food process the apples with the orange juice. Serve just as it is, delicately warm. Stir in some virtually-no-fat fromage frais for an occasional variation (but add an extra 14 calories).

INSTANT PORRIDGE IN A PLATE

CALORIES PER SERVING: 222
SERVES: 1

VARIATIONS
1. Use rolled oats instead of the more nutritious wholegrain oatmeal; this will produce a more jellied porridge.
2. Omit nuts and seeds for plain porridge.
3. Add dried fruits, coconut chips or other tasty items as liked.
4. Substitute skimmed milk and honey for yogurt and sugar.

2tbsp medium stoneground oatmeal (not rolled oats)
1tsp seeds: linseed, sesame or sunflower
1tbsp chopped or broken nuts: pecans, almonds, walnuts
⅛tsp salt
8tbsp hand-hot tap water
1tbsp wheatgerm (optional)
2tbsp low-fat natural yogurt
1tsp soft dark brown sugar

Measure the first 5 ingredients into a microwave-proof soup bowl or porridge plate. Stir.

Microwave, uncovered, on HIGH for 1½ minutes. Using the flat of a fork, stir vigorously to mix the sides and base to the centre. Microwave, uncovered, on HIGH for another minute. Stir again, adding the wheatgerm if liked. Serve hot with yogurt and sugar.

LOW-FAT CITRUS, NUT & SEED MUESLI

SELECT YOUR OWN FAVOURITES TO 'CUSTOMIZE' THIS DELICIOUS 'HIGH-NUTRITION' MUESLI.
MAKE UP A BATCH AT WEEKENDS. IT'S EASY IF YOU ASSEMBLE EVERYTHING BEFORE YOU START.
THE RECIPE HERE MAKES ENOUGH MUESLI FOR A 2-PERSON HOUSEHOLD FOR 9 DAYS, THOUGH YOU MAY
FIND YOU USE IT ON FRUIT, CUSTARD AND AS A CRUMBLE TOPPING TOO.

CALORIES PER SERVING: 217
SERVES: 18

BIRCHER MUESLI

Pour 4tbsp boiling water over 2tbsp rolled oats and add ¼ tsp seasalt. Leave to stand for 5–10 minutes. Add the grated zest (optional) and diced flesh of ½ an orange. Add 1 cored apple, in small cubes, 1tbsp each of wheatgerm, sun-dried raisins, walnut pieces and honey. Stir then add 4tbsp low-fat natural bio-yogurt.

CALORIES PER SERVING: 345
SERVES: 1

grated rind and juice of 1 small orange
125g/4oz flower-scented honey or malt syrup
50g/2oz dark muscovado sugar
2tsp mixed spice
1tsp vanilla essence
2tsp seasalt flakes
50g/2oz oatbran or wheat bran
85g/3oz wheatgerm or oat germ
250g/9oz rolled oats
50g/2oz seeds: sesame and/or sunflower or pumpkin
50g/2oz nuts: pinenuts and/or pistachios or almonds
225g/8oz dried fruit: apricots and/or apples, pears or prunes, scissor-chopped

Combine the first 6 ingredients in a large 4 litre/7 pint, 25cm/10in diameter microwave-proof casserole. Microwave, uncovered, on HIGH for 4 minutes or until the mixture bubbles vigorously.

Meanwhile, assemble and mix the remaining ingredients apart from the dried fruit. When the syrup is ready, stir in these dry ingredients quickly and microwave, uncovered, on HIGH for 9 minutes longer. After 8 minutes, add the dried fruits and stir the mixture from the sides to the centre.

Tip the hot, browned, aromatic muesli out on to a large tray. Cool completely. Break up any big chunks and store in an airtight jar in a cool dark place. Eat with low-fat yogurt or skimmed milk.

RISOGALO CREAMY RICE

CALORIES PER SERVING: 230
SERVES: 4

This creamy rice custard, inspired by cool Greek coffee-house fare, is good eaten both hot and warm. Cold it makes the next day's breakfast. It is really versatile and tastes superb topped with fresh peaches or melon. Try it instead of yogurt for a change.

85g/3oz short-grain pudding-type rice
750ml/1¼ pints semi-skimmed milk
2 eggs (size 3), separated
pinch of salt
50g/2oz caster sugar
¼ tsp ground cinnamon

Put the rice and 600ml/1 pint of the milk in a large, high-sided (at least 12.5cm/5in) microwave-proof mixing bowl. Microwave, un-covered, on HIGH for 25 minutes. Give it a stir after 10 and 20 minutes.

After the second stir, whisk the egg whites with the salt until frothy. Add the sugar and whisk until the whites will form peaks that flop over.

Stir the egg yolks into the hot cooked rice, then stir in the remaining milk. Microwave, uncovered, on HIGH for 2 minutes to reheat briefly and thicken.

Fold the egg white into the hot creamy rice. Microwave, uncovered, on HIGH for a final minute. Stir, spoon into bowls and dust with the spice. Serve hot. To serve warm, cover and allow to cool to room temperature. If serving cold, stir in 6tbsp of iced water before adding the spice: once cold the set is firmer.

PERFECT POACHED EGGS

TO POACH AN EGG SUCCESSFULLY IN A MICROWAVE: 1. PIERCE THE YOLK AND WHITE CAREFULLY IN SEVERAL PLACES USING A COCKTAIL STICK; 2. EXPECT THE YOLK TO COOK QUICKER THAN THE WHITE; 3. EXPECT ROOM TEMPERATURE EGGS TO COOK MORE EVENLY THAN CHILLED EGGS.

CALORIES PER SERVING: 74
SERVES: 1

NOTE: For 2 eggs, allow 2–2¼ minutes; after 1½ minutes, change the positions and check the set, cooking longer if wished.

2tbsp boiling water
1 fresh egg (size 3), at room temperature
seasalt flakes and freshly ground black pepper

Measure the boiling water into a microwave-proof container. (A 7.5cm/3in diameter, 150ml/¼ pint volume ramekin or a glass measuring jug works well.)

Break in the egg and pierce the membranes carefully several times. Microwave, uncovered, on MEDIUM (50%) for 1¼ –1½ minutes, checking for doneness after the shorter time. Continue cooking as needed.

Drain the egg and season. Eat from the ramekin or else set out on a toasted muffin half (77 extra calories).

COCOTTE EGGS

ONCE UPON A TIME BAKED EGGS REQUIRED A BAIN MARIE, PREHEATING THE OVEN AND MILITARY PRECISION. THESE LITTLE POTS OF MICROWAVED EGGS, FLAVOURED WITH A FEW AROMATICS, ARE A PUSHOVER. PERFECT FOR BREAKFAST, BRUNCH OR EVEN LUNCH SNACKS

CALORIES PER SERVING: 118
SERVES: 2

VARIATIONS
1. Omit the tomato. Substitute 4 cooked peeled prawn tails or 25g/1oz flaked smoked fish.
2. Omit the fromage frais. Substitute pesto or tapenade, plus a little cubed tomato flesh and black pepper.

NOTE: For 1 serving, halve the ingredients and microwave on MEDIUM (50%) for 1 minute 20 seconds.

1tsp butter or oil
2 eggs (size 3), at room temperature
2tbsp virtually-no-fat fromage frais
1tsp scissor-chopped fresh herbs: parsley, tarragon
1tsp scissor-chopped sun-dried tomatoes
15g/½ oz grated half-fat Cheddar cheese

Divide the butter between two microwave-proof china or glass cocottes (about 7.5cm/3in diameter). Microwave, uncovered, on HIGH for 30 seconds. Break an egg into each cocotte. Carefully pierce the membrane of each yolk and white in several places with a pin or cocktail stick. Spoon fromage frais, herbs, tomatoes and cheese on to each. Microwave, uncovered, on MEDIUM (50%) for about 3 minutes. Serve hot.

TOFU MALT SHAKE

CALORIES PER SERVING: 69
SERVES: 4

VARIATION
Add a little instant coffee powder if liked.

A velvety breakfast drink in seconds, for those who prefer not to drink cow's milk. (Skimmed milk, however, could equally well be substituted.)

Put 500ml/17floz soy milk plus 6 ice cubes, 2tbsp barley malt syrup and 4tsp cocoa powder into a blender, food processor or screw-top jar. Blend, whizz or shake until frothy. Serve in a glass with straws.

PERFECT POACHED EGGS

BACON & TOMATO BREAKFAST

BACON & TOMATO BREAKFAST

MICROWAVED BACON IS NOT EXACTLY CRUNCHY BUT THE TASTE AND COLOUR ARE
ABSOLUTELY FINE. AFTER THIS THE CLASSIC 'FRY-UP' WILL SEEM OBSOLETE. LEAN STREAKY
PROVIDES EXCELLENT FLAVOUR, THOUGH YOU MIGHT PREFER LEAN BACK BACON.

CALORIES PER SERVING: 224
SERVES: 2

NOTE: To double the recipe, repeat
the process.

*2 flavourful tomatoes,
about 150g/5oz*

*4 rashers of smoked, sweetcure,
streaky bacon (about 85g/3oz)*

*scissor-chopped fresh herbs:
parsley, chives, dill, etc*

Halve the tomatoes crosswise. Set
them, with the rashers of bacon,
on a ridged microwave roasting
utensil (this drains off fat and
juices and makes cooking
efficient).

Microwave, uncovered, on
HIGH for 5 minutes. Sprinkle herbs
over the tomatoes and serve.
(Keep the delicious juices to use in
other dishes such as in mashed
potatoes or on green vegetables.)

TWO-MINUTE TOMATOES ON TOAST

CALORIES PER SERVING: 129
(PLUS 80 FOR TOAST)
SERVES: 1

VARIATIONS
1. Omit the oil completely for a very
lean version, or add a poached egg
instead.
2. Substitute garlic butter for oil and
some chopped spring onions in place
of herbs. Spoon over ciabatta, plain or
toasted.

*2 ripe, flavourful tomatoes
(about 175g/6oz each)*

2tsp extra virgin olive oil

salt and freshly ground black pepper

*fresh herbs: basil, tarragon,
chives, parsley or coriander*

*1 slice of wholewheat bread,
toasted*

Halve the tomatoes lengthwise (so
they sit flat), then cross-slice using
a sharp serrated knife. Put into
a microwave-proof ring dish.
Drizzle the oil over them.
Microwave, uncovered, on HIGH
for 2 minutes whilst making toast.

Remove the cooked tomatoes
and stir so they form their own
creamy sauce. Season to taste and
add torn herbs of choice. Pour
over the hot toast and serve.

SMOKED MACKEREL TOAST TOPPER

CALORIES PER SERVING: 26 (2TBSP
EACH)
SERVES: 12

This potted fish spread, if eaten daily,
guarantees few calories but provides
useful Omega-3 polyunsaturates needed
for a healthy heart. It's best on crusty
toast, French bread or matzoh crackers.
Great for breakfast on the run, brunch
or open sandwiches, so always keep a
pot in the fridge.

*125g/4oz smoked mackerel fillets,
skinned and flaked*

2 garlic cloves, crushed (optional)

1tsp tomato paste

*1tsp anchovy paste (Patum Peperium)
or 1 canned anchovy, chopped*

*200g/7oz quark (1% fat skim milk
soft cheese)*

2tbsp freshly squeezed lemon juice

15g/½ oz parsley stalks

Put all but the last ingredient into a
food processor or blender. Process
to a paste, stopping the machine
now and then to scrape down the
mixture from sides to centre.

Scissor-chop the parsley stalks
into a heatproof sieve. Pour over
some boiling water and shake well
to drain. Add the herbs to the
paste. Process briefly once more.

Spoon into a lidded pot. Use
straight away or chill until slightly
more firm.

Spread 2tbsp on a slice of
wholegrain, unbuttered toast for
an instant breakfast.

SOUPS & SNACKS:
THE PLEASURE PRINCIPLE

The more you think about what you shouldn't eat, the more food can become obsessional. Snatched late or early meals, between-meal fuel stops, little bits and pieces to fill in the hunger gap between lunchtime and your evening meal – all are important enough to warrant good-quality, interesting foods.

It is here that a too-rigid, too-boring or over-elaborate diet system will let you down. Lunch, brunch and supper should provide a third of daily energy requirements, so enjoy them and let them be lively and varied. Eat for pleasure, and try not to binge or starve out of guilt.

For the health-conscious dieter and the emancipated cook these meals must be delicious but relaxed, fibre-high certainly (fruit and vegetables are the key) but quick and easy to make. This is when the microwave is a real boon.

Most people's weekday lunchtimes, alas, must be brief, but often it's the peak time for your digestion: your body is in excellent metabolizing mood at midday so give it some positive help.

Microwave-cooked snacks, picnic food, office lunches and more sedate supper recipes can all be found in this chapter. Four time-tested lunch formulae are: a salad (hot or cold) with a roll; an open sandwich followed by raw fruit; microwave-baked potatoes plus tasty additions, then yogurt; and, finally, soup and toast, then cheese and/or fruit. All of these make easy, decent meal patterns.

Of the recipes in this section, few contain meat as the main event. Fish and shellfish crop up in spreads with chickpeas, in oyster risotto, with pasta, in a sizzle of prawns cooked with ginger and garlic, or as soup garnishes. Oily fish (salmon and kippers, for example) contain Omega-3 oils, valuable for heart health and general circulatory well being. Peas and beans along with other grain products (cracked wheat, couscous and even popcorn with a coating of nuts and seeds) and five sensational soups provide comfort and a feast of flavours from basil, ginger and beetroot to sweet potato, roasted red peppers and saffron. A vegetarian sushi and some pretty pasta dishes suitable for any occasion mainly hinge on the 'liberated larder' principle, so need minimal shopping time or effort to make well. Asian dishes (crispy poppadums for example, but the low-fat kind that you never dreamed were possible), Italian, Spanish and Russian influences, along with Mexican-style tacos and Middle Eastern tabbouleh and couscous, help make up this cross-cultural collection. And never far away, the essential ingredients to keep us slim, well and satisfied: a bonanza of fruits, vegetables and herbs.

LEFT: POLENTA PIZZA WITH SUN-DRIED TOMATOES; LOW-FAT POPPADUMS

POLENTA PIZZA
WITH SUN-DRIED TOMATOES

NEVER HAS PIZZA BEEN SO EARTHY, LIVELY, LOW IN FAT AND QUICK! VINE-RIPENED
TOMATOES, AUTHENTIC MOZZARELLA AND TASTY OLIVES ADD MUCH TO THE FINAL RESULT,
SO IT IS A MUST TO SHOP CAREFULLY.

CALORIES PER SERVING: 189
SERVES: 6

SERVING SUGGESTIONS
1. Serve with a salad of crisp lettuce heart, raw spinach, celery and herbs.
2. One slice of pizza with coleslaw, iced mineral water and an apple makes good lunchbox fare.
3. Dice cucumber into a small pot of low-fat natural bio-yogurt. Add fresh mint and crisp cos lettuce leaves. Serve with pizza for a light supper. Follow with melon.

175g/6oz fine cornmeal (polenta)
125g/4oz strong wholemeal flour
1 tbsp baking powder
½ tsp salt
½ tsp dried crushed chillies
300g/11oz virtually-no-fat fromage frais
1 egg, beaten
TOPPING
2tbsp tomato purée
6 medium plum tomatoes, chopped
4 garlic cloves, chopped
40g/1½ oz sun-dried tomatoes, drained
100g/3½ oz low-fat mozzarella cheese, drained and thinly sliced
10 Greek-style black olives, stoned
15g/½ oz (1 handful) torn fresh basil leaves

Mix together the first 5 ingredients. Add the fromage frais and egg and whisk together with a fork, then mix to a soft dough. Knead 3 or 4 times. Pat out on baking parchment to a 25cm/10in diameter circle. Set on a microwave-proof serving plate, if wished.

Microwave, uncovered, on HIGH for 6 minutes or so or until the dough feels firm on top and around the edges but with a little give towards the centre.

Quickly spread the tomato purée right to the edges. Top with chopped tomatoes, garlic and a border of sun-dried tomatoes. Cover the central two-thirds with mozzarella. Scatter on the olives.

Microwave, uncovered, on MEDIUM (50%) for 8 minutes and then on HIGH for 3 minutes.

Add the basil. Leave to stand for 2 minutes and then serve hot.

LOW-FAT POPPADUMS

THE NEAREST TO MICROWAVE MAGIC YOU'LL EVER SEE: PURCHASED INDIAN POPPADUMS
(CHICKPEA FLOUR ROUND WAFERS) THAT RISE, WRINKLE AND COOK RIGHT BEFORE YOUR EYES.
NONE OF THE USUAL ADDED FAT, NO GRILL FIRES, FEWER CALORIES!

CALORIES PER SERVING: 120
(2 POPPADUMS EACH)
SERVES: 4

NOTE: For 1 poppadum, allow approx. 1 minute.

8 poppadums or pappad: garlic, spiced or plain

Put the poppadums, 2 at a time, between 2 sheets of kitchen paper. Microwave on HIGH for 2–2½ minutes (depending on size or type); halfway through, turn them over and reverse their positions. Serve alone as snacks or with dips and curries.

NACHOS WITH MELTED CHEESE

SIMPLE SNACK FOOD FOR AVID APPETITES, RUSTLED UP FROM YOUR LARDER AND
FRIDGE. YOUR YOUNG CAN MAKE THESE THEMSELVES AT HOME, RATHER THAN SPENDING
A FORTUNE AT THE TAKE-AWAY.

CALORIES PER SERVING: 136
SERVES: 4

SERVING SUGGESTION
Serve with Coriander Guacamole
(page 121).

*125g/4oz low-fat Cheddar
cheese, grated*
1tsp celery or garlic salt
1tsp sweet chilli sauce
2tsp wine vinegar or pickle juice
1tbsp hot water
*24 corn chips (tortilla chips
or nachips)*
*15g/½oz (1tbsp) sliced pickled
chillies, gherkins or capers*

Mix the cheese with the salt, sauce,
vinegar and water. Sprinkle some
of this mixture over each of the
corn chips arranged around the
edge of a microwave-proof serving
plate. Scatter chillies (or other
chosen topping) over all.

Microwave, uncovered, on
MEDIUM (50%) for 2–3 minutes
or until the cheese has melted and
the nachos smell aromatic. Leave
to stand for 30 seconds, then
serve piping hot.

ONE-DISH MACARONI CHEESE

NO DRAINING, NO MESS, NO SAUCE STICKING TO THE PAN, ALL IN ONE DISH AND DELICIOUS.
GENEROUS SERVINGS OF MICROWAVED MACARONI CHEESE MAKE INEXPENSIVE SNACK LUNCH OR SUPPER
SOLUTIONS. CELERY AND SPINACH SALAD, CRISPBREADS AND THEN FRESH PEARS PARTNER THIS WELL.

CALORIES PER SERVING: 399
SERVES: 4

NOTE: For 2 servings, halve the
quantities and allow 10–12 minutes.

25g/1oz butter
*200g/7oz 'quick-cook' pasta:
macaroni or conchigliette*
6 spring onions or ¼ leek, shredded
2 garlic cloves, chopped
750ml/1¼ pints boiling water
1tsp seasalt flakes
¼ tsp paprika
*150g/5oz cheese: Red Leicester,
Double Gloucester or Cheddar,
grated*
2tbsp flour
3tbsp low-fat natural yogurt
1 celery stick, finely sliced

Put the butter, pasta, most of the
spring onions, the garlic, boiling
water and salt in a large microwave-
proof measuring jug. Stir, then
microwave, uncovered, on HIGH
for 12–14 minutes (check packet
instructions) or until the pasta is
tender and most of the water has
been absorbed.

Mix in the paprika, grated
cheese, flour and yogurt.
Microwave, uncovered, on HIGH
for 3 minutes or until the cheese
has melted and the mixture
bubbles at the edges. Leave to
stand for 1 minute. Sprinkle with
the celery and remaining spring
onions and serve.

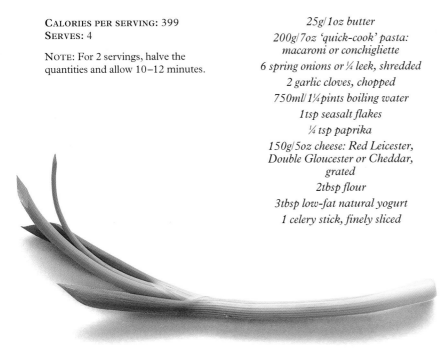

HOME-STYLE BURGERS

HERE'S A HOMELY, HEALTHY RETHINK OF A 'FAST-FOOD' FAVOURITE. MICROWAVE-COOKING
LEAN MEAT WITHOUT ADDED FAT (AND WITH FRUIT AND HIGH-FIBRE CRUMBS ADDED TO THE MIX)
GIVES A SOFTER RESULT BUT HELPS KEEP CALORIES LOWER THAN THE BOUGHT EQUIVALENT.
TASTES GOOD TOO.

CALORIES PER SERVING: 260
(2 BURGERS WITHOUT BREAD)
SERVES: 4 (OR 8 AS A SNACK)

SERVING SUGGESTIONS
Plum tomatoes, sliced avocado and
extra lettuce, if liked.

OPTIONAL EXTRA BROWNING
Preheat a browning dish in the
microwave on HIGH for 5 minutes
(or according to manufacturer's
instructions). Lightly paint the cooked
burgers on one side only with a little
olive oil. Sizzle them, oiled side down,
on the dish for 1½ minutes then turn
over and cook the other side. (This
deepens the colour and increases
firmness, but the meat shrinks more
and may crumble slightly.)

*125g/4oz stale wholewheat
bread, cubed*

1 crisp apple, cored and cubed

*450g/1lb extra-lean minced turkey,
chicken, veal or lamb*

*15g/½oz fresh herbs: thyme
or parsley*

1tsp dried crushed chillies

4 garlic cloves, crushed

*2tsp coriander seeds, roughly
crushed*

3tbsp rich soy sauce

*2tbsp each hoisin sauce and sweet
chilli sauce, mixed*

*SERVING ACCOMPANIMENTS:
8 baps: wholewheat or sesame,
split in half*

4tbsp American Pickles (page 117)

*2 Little Gem lettuces or ½ cos or
iceberg lettuce*

2 red peppers, seeded and sliced

Put the cubed bread and apple
into a food processor. Process
until crumb-like. Add the next
6 ingredients and half of the
hoisin-chilli sauce mixture to the
food processor. Process briefly,
scraping the mixture down from
the sides once or twice, until a
ball forms.

Divide the mixture into 8. Pat
out each portion into an untidy
7.5cm/3in diameter round.

Set the burger patties around
the edge of a large microwave-
proof platter. Cover with kitchen
paper. Microwave on HIGH for
6 minutes; halfway through,
reposition the burgers (turning
them around, outer edge to
inside).

Turn the burgers over. Brush
the remaining hoisin-chilli sauce
over the top surface. Microwave,
uncovered, on HIGH for 2−3
minutes more. Leave to stand for
1 minute (the colour will darken).

To assemble, spread the cut
surface of a half bap with pickle,
then top with lettuce leaves and a
burger. Finish with red pepper
slices. Serve hot (if necessary,
reheat briefly).

RAW MUSHROOM VINAIGRETTE

CALORIES PER SERVING: 134
SERVES: 2

Raw fungi with herbs and a decent dressing have real class.

Wipe 125g/4oz fresh mushrooms (buttons, chestnut mushrooms, shiitake, or oyster mushrooms) free of grit or soil. Slice wafer thin. Add juice of 1 lemon. Measure over 1tsp balsamic vinegar, 2tbsp extra virgin olive oil, then 15g/½oz fresh herbs: chives, parsley, tarragon or chervil or a mixture,

scissor chopped. Stir gently. Season with seasalt and freshly ground black pepper or crushed coriander seeds. Serve immediately or some time later as a snack, appetizer, sandwich topping or salad component, or as a delicious baked potato topper (see recipe below).

BAKED POTATO 'TOPPERS'

MICROWAVED POTATOES COOK BRILLIANTLY AND QUICKLY. THOUGH THE LACK OF CRISP SKIN COMES AS RATHER A SHOCK, THE FLUFFY, FULL-FLAVOURED FLESH IS AMPLE COMPENSATION. POTATOES WITH FLAVOURFUL TOPPINGS CAN BECOME AN EASY LIGHT MEAL, FAST SNACK, LATE SUPPER OR LEAN LUNCH.

CALORIES PER SERVING: 302
SERVES: 4

VARIATIONS
1. Add 2tbsp Hummus-Kipper Pâté (page 50) per potato and fresh coriander sprigs. Do not reheat.
2. Add 2tbsp Tapenade with Mushrooms (page 122) per potato with some fresh basil, and 1 plum tomato, sliced. Do not reheat.
3. Add 1tsp Pesto with Pistachios (page 121) per potato with ¼ red pepper, cubed. Do not reheat.
4. Add 4 raw mangetouts, shredded, 15g/½oz feta cheese, cubed, 1 fresh mint sprig and 1tbsp natural bio-yogurt per potato. Do not reheat.
5. Add 2tbsp Tamarillo Relish (page 117), 25g/1oz diced cooked chicken and some watercress per potato. Do not reheat.
6. Add 2tbsp Tandoori Cheese Dip (page 124), ¼ yellow pepper, cubed, and a few capers per potato. Do not reheat.

4 x 200g/7oz baking potatoes: floury potatoes of good flavour such as Cara, Pentland Squire, Pentland Crown

TOPPINGS:
8 sun-dried tomatoes
4 spring onions
50g/2oz meltable cheese: Gruyère, Fontina or other
2tsp extra virgin olive oil
freshly ground seasalt and black pepper

Pierce each potato in 4 places. Arrange them in a ring on kitchen paper in the microwave and cover with another sheet of kitchen paper. Microwave on HIGH for 14–18 minutes; halfway through, turn them over top to bottom.

Foil-wrap the potatoes in one large parcel and leave to stand for the 5 minutes it takes to prepare the toppings.

Scissor-shred the dried tomatoes, slice the spring onions and slice the (chilled) cheese into 20–24 slivers.

Unwrap the cooked potatoes. Slice off a thickish lid from each. Ruffle the potato flesh quickly, using two forks. Add the oil, cheese, spring onions and then tomatoes. Season to taste. Reheat, unwrapped, on HIGH for 45 seconds more or until the cheese trickles deliciously.

HUMMUS-KIPPER PATÉ

THIS IS MY NEW VERSION OF HUMMUS: WITHOUT THE USUAL OIL BUT WITH KIPPER AND LIME
TO BOOST FLAVOUR, VITAMIN VALUE AND PROTEIN LEVELS. EASY, GOOD AND POSSIBLE IN UNDER
10 MINUTES. EXCELLENT FOR SANDWICHES, PICNICS AND PARTIES.

CALORIES PER SERVING: 120
(50G/2OZ EACH)
SERVES: 8 (MAKES 500G/1LB 2OZ)

125g/4oz boneless kipper fillets
439g/15oz canned chickpeas, drained
2 garlic cloves, crushed
1tbsp tahini (sesame paste)
shredded zest of 1 lime and juice of 2 limes
pinch of chilli powder
watercress, cucumber and small crisp lettuce leaves to garnish

Arrange the kipper fillets in a shallow microwave-proof casserole. Sprinkle with a little water. Microwave, covered, on HIGH for 1 minute. Flake the drained fish quickly with forks, discarding skin and any bones.

Put the chickpeas, garlic, tahini, lime zest and juice and chilli powder in a food processor. Process in short bursts to a rough paste. Add the kipper and process again until fairly smooth. Chill until firm in a lidded pot or terrine. Keeps, chilled, for up to 7 days.

Serve several small scoops of pâté per person (no more than 50g/2oz each) on a bed of watercress with cucumber, rocket and red lettuce. Use the remainder as a breakfast toast-topper spread or on crusty French bread.

SMOKED OYSTER RISOTTO

CALORIES PER SERVING: 280
SERVES: 4

A carefree, hardly stirred risotto, but you'll need some exotics first: fish sauce (also called fish soy) and Japanese soy sauce (both available from Oriental stores). Together these create a sea-scented, delicate dish.

Smoked oysters add epicurean charm but use fresh ones, if available, icy cold and on the half shell, for a last-minute garnish. Lush but lovely.

225g/8oz easy-cook long-grain brown rice
1 tsp fish sauce
600ml/1 pint boiling water
1tsp salt
2 garlic cloves, shredded
1 red onion, halved and sliced
3 tbsp Japanese soy sauce
150ml/¼ pint boiling water
1 tbsp walnut oil
2 × 105g/4oz cans smoked oysters, drained
8 crisp green lettuce leaves, shredded
4 spring onions, sliced
15g/½ oz parsley, chopped
lemon wedges
4–6 fresh oysters (optional)

Combine the first 3 ingredients, in order, in a 25cm/10in diameter microwave-proof casserole.

Cover and microwave on HIGH for 22 minutes. Uncover, add the next 4 ingredients and the second measure of boiling water and stir. Cover again and microwave for a further 8 minutes or until the rice is very plump and tender and the water almost all absorbed.

Uncover and stir in the oil and smoked oysters. Microwave, uncovered, for 3 more minutes. Cover and leave to stand for 2 minutes.

Make a border of lettuce and spring onion on each plate. Spoon the risotto into the centre and sprinkle with parsley. Have lemon wedges for squeezing over and fresh oysters left on their half shells, if available, as a final, ice-cold garnish.

PEPPER & GOAT'S CHEESE PASTE

CALORIES PER SERVING: 68
SERVES: 6

SERVING SUGGESTION
Serve a portion as a spread for soda
bread, savoury muffins or crackers or
as a large open sandwich, with radishes,
watercress or baby spinach leaves
on top.

VARIATIONS
1. Use as a dip with raw crisp green
salad vegetables or with melon.
2. Thinned a little (use equal parts
of white wine) it can be spooned over
avocado slices, celery, chicory and
watercress as a salad dressing.
3. Use blue cheese instead of goat's
cheese, and dry sherry instead of
grappa. Serve with hot toast.
4. Use Munster instead of goat's cheese
and substitute a pear eau-de-vie.

1 large pepper: yellow or orange,
pierced 2 or 3 times
50g/2 oz pungent goat's cheese,
crumbled
100g/3½ oz low-fat soft cheese
1tbsp grappa or brandy
pinch of powdered saffron (⅟₁₆ tsp)
1tbsp extra virgin olive oil
¼ tsp salt
freshly ground pepper

Brush the whole, pierced pepper
with olive oil and put it in a
microwave roasting bag. Tuck the
ends under to seal, or seal loosely
with a bag tie. Microwave on
HIGH for 4–5 minutes; halfway
through, turn the bag and contents

over. Remove from the microwave
oven and seal the bag tightly with a
rubber band. Leave undisturbed
to cool.

Slide the skin off the pepper,
using kitchen paper if necessary,
and discard skin, seeds, stalk and
membranes. Chop the flesh
roughly. Put it into a food
processor, blender or mortar with
the 2 cheeses. Process or blend in
short bursts, or pound with a
pestle, to a paste, incorporating the
grappa, saffron and olive oil.
Taste and season as wished.

Refrigerate (for up to a week)
in a lidded pot.

FIONA'S BORSCHT WITH CORIANDER

CALORIES PER SERVING: 223
SERVES: 4

Borscht made in the microwave is a
revelation, and since raw beetroot is
known to benefit the digestive system
and the liver it is a pity to ignore its
charms. This is a vivid soup, seething
with colour, taste and life, rather like my
friend Fiona, after whom I named it.

1tbsp extra virgin olive oil
225g/8oz carrots, sliced
225g/8oz red onion, sliced
4 garlic cloves, chopped
125g/4oz bulb fennel, sliced crosswise
225g/8oz potatoes, scrubbed, in
1.5cm/½ in dice
1 vegetable stock cube, crumbled
1.1 litres/2 pints boiling water
1tbsp rich soy sauce
12 parsley stalks, tied with string,
crushed
450g/1lb raw or cooked beetroot,
in 5mm/¼ in cubes
1–1½ tsp dried crushed chillies
15g/½ oz dried mushrooms: ceps,
morels
2–3tbsp fruit vinegar: blackcurrant,
raspberry
4 sprigs of fresh coriander leaves,
crushed
15g/½ oz seeds: fennel or dill
100g/3½oz fromage frais (8% fat)

Combine the oil, carrots, onion
and garlic in a large microwave-
proof casserole (4 litre/7 pint
volume). Microwave, uncovered,
on HIGH for 3 minutes, stirring
halfway through. Add the next
6 ingredients and raw beetroot (if
using). Cover and microwave on
HIGH for a further 8 minutes.

Discard the parsley. Stir in the
crushed chillies, cooked beetroot
(if using) and the dried
mushrooms. Microwave, covered,
on HIGH for a final 12 minutes.

Add some vinegar and stir well,
then adjust to taste. Serve the soup
hot with 5 floating coriander leaves
in each generous bowlful. Have
freshly toasted seeds (microwave-
warmed to aromatic on HIGH for
2 minutes) and fromage frais in
little bowls to add to the soup.

This soup is superb eaten up to
3 days later, hot or chilled.

Capsicum Soup Ortiz; Green Velvet Soup

GREEN VELVET SOUP

CALORIES PER SERVING: 110
SERVES: 4

A glamorous but highly nutritious soup of roots and greens. Serve it in generous mugs or bowls with some crisp crackers, unbuttered toast fingers or crusty rolls. Vary ingredients according to season and whim.

VARIATIONS
1. Use Jerusalem artichoke in place of sweet potato.
2. Use Swiss chard or spinach beet instead of spinach.
3. For a West Indian version, substitute yams for sweet potato, callaloo leaves (dasheen or arvi leaf) for spinach and chilli seasoning for curry. Add a 25g/1oz chunk of creamed coconut (chopped).

2 garlic cloves, crushed
250g/9oz carrot, scrubbed and sliced
250g/9oz sweet potato, scrubbed, in 1.5cm/½in cubes
600ml/1 pint boiling well-flavoured vegetable stock
225g/8oz spinach leaves
150ml/¼ pint semi-skimmed milk
½ tsp curry powder
½ tsp salt
freshly ground black pepper

Put the garlic, carrot and sweet potato in a large, microwave-proof casserole (2.5 litre/4¼ pint volume) with half the boiling stock. Microwave, covered, on HIGH for 8 minutes.

Reserve a few spinach leaves: roughly tear the rest and add to the casserole. Microwave on HIGH for a further 4 minutes or until the spinach is a brilliant green.

Purée the contents of the casserole in batches, using a blender (a food processor gives a less velvety result). Pour back into the casserole and add the remaining stock, the milk, curry powder, salt, and pepper to taste. Microwave, covered, on HIGH for the 4 minutes it takes to bring back to boiling point. Whisk, then serve with the reserved shredded spinach on top.

CAPSICUM SOUP ORTIZ

CALORIES PER SERVING: 55
SERVES: 4

This pretty red spicy soup can enliven any meal. Though extremely simple to make (less than 20 minutes), it has a suave fruity flavour. Dress it up with flowers for special occasions.

In summer, you can chill the soup and serve it icy cold.

2 × 225g/8oz red peppers
2tsp harissa (hot chilli paste)
8tbsp virtually-no-fat fromage frais
½ tsp seasalt
450ml/¾ pint boiling well-flavoured vegetable stock
32 fresh coriander leaves (optional)
15g/½ oz edible flowers: nasturtiums, violas (optional)

Preheat a large 25cm/10in browning dish in the microwave for 8 minutes (or according to manufacturer's instructions). Meanwhile, cut off stalk and base ends of the peppers, then split the tubes of pepper flesh down one side so they can be rolled out flat.

Open the microwave and, without removing the browning dish, quickly add the peppers, skins down, to the hot pan. Flatten them with a heavy microwave-proof plate. Microwave (plate and all) on HIGH for 8 minutes or until aromatic: halfway through, give the pan a quarter turn.

Scissor-chop the soft peppers with their brown-blotched skins. Put half into a blender (a food processor gives a rougher, less satisfactory result). Add half the harissa, one-quarter of the fromage frais and half the salt. Process in short bursts to a purée. Add half the boiling stock (microwaved on HIGH for 3 minutes) and purée again. Repeat the process with the remaining peppers.

Serve warm, with dollops of fromage frais, floating coriander leaves and the flowers if wished. If the soup is preferred very hot, reheat it, covered, on HIGH for 4–5 minutes or so until steaming. Stir, then garnish and serve.

ALMOST-INSTANT SOUP

HALF AN HOUR AFTER OPENING THE DOOR AND TURNING ON THE KETTLE, YOU CAN BE
DRINKING ELEGANT FRESH HOME-MADE CLEAR SOUP. VARY GARNISHES ACCORDING TO YOUR MOOD,
THE SEASONS AND YOUR FINANCES.

CALORIES PER SERVING: 45
SERVES: 4

GARNISH VARIATIONS
1. Torn spinach, bean sprouts, cured
ham shreds, sliced radishes.
2. Powdered saffron (microwave on
HIGH for 3–4 minutes), sliced cooked
lobster, fresh lemon slices, lettuce shreds.
3. Smoked salmon shreds, keta, pink
peppercorns, fresh coriander leaves.
4. Cooked peeled prawns, fresh chives
and tarragon, star anise pods.
5. Pumpkin or butternut squash slivers,
okra and borlotti beans (microwave-
cook vegetables for 5–6 minutes or
until tender).

1tbsp flavourful dried mushrooms:
ceps, morels
1 carrot, quartered (unpeeled)
1 onion, quartered (unskinned)
1 tomato, quartered (unskinned)
1 celery stick, quartered
10 parsley stalks, quartered
1 small dried chilli, seeded
2.5cm/1in piece of fresh root ginger,
quartered (optional)
2 garlic cloves, crushed
1.1 litres/2 pints boiling water
seasalt and freshly ground
black pepper
fresh herbs: parsley, chives and/or
chervil to garnish (optional)

Put the first 9 ingredients, in
batches, into a food processor,

with the machine running, and
chop them very small. Scrape out
into a large microwave-proof
casserole. Add the boiling water,
stir and cover with a lid. Wrap
the whole casserole tightly with
2 layers of microwave-safe
clingfilm, unpierced.

Microwave on HIGH for 20
minutes. Use tongs to unwrap the
casserole and then pour the soup
into a non-metal sieve set over a
microwave-proof bowl. Press well
on the solids, then discard them.

Microwave, loosely covered, on
HIGH for 4–5 minutes or until hot.
Season the soup well to taste and
add the herbs.

BUTTERFLY PASTA, BRESAOLA & PEAS

CALORIES PER SERVING: 296
SERVES: 6

Some too-dense pasta cooks badly in the
microwave, but smallish dried butterfly
pasta shapes cook well. Bresaola replaces
bacon, fromage frais supplants cream yet
the taste is utterly
voluptuous.

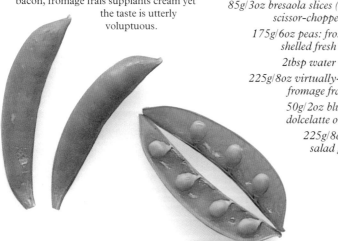

350g/12oz dry or fresh farfalle
(butterflies)
salt
1 tbsp extra virgin olive oil
4 garlic cloves, crushed
85g/3oz bresaola slices (cured beef),
scissor-chopped
175g/6oz peas: frozen or
shelled fresh
2tbsp water
225g/8oz virtually-no-fat
fromage frais
50g/2oz blue cheese:
dolcelatte or gorgonzola
225g/8oz prepared
salad greens, torn

Put the pasta in a large (at least
25cm/10in diameter) microwave-
proof casserole. Pour over a
kettleful of boiling water and add
some salt. Microwave, covered,
on HIGH for 10 minutes. Leave to
stand while you make the sauce,
still covered.

Combine the oil, garlic,
bresaola, peas and water in a large
microwave-proof measuring jug.
Microwave, uncovered, on HIGH
for 3 minutes or until aromatic.
Add the fromage frais and blue
cheese. Microwave on LOW (30%)
for 4 minutes. Stir well.

Drain the pasta, toss in the
sauce and spoon on to the salad
greens.

VEGETABLE POTTAGE

CALORIES PER SERVING: 195
SERVES: 8

Chunky vegetable soup with a
countrified taste, but easily made in
about 20 minutes, is a cheering idea.
Substitute leftover home-cooked beans
or diced potato for kidney beans, if liked,
adding a little extra water. For a
substantial course, say with bread and
cheese followed by pears, double the
serving size to serve 4.

100g/3½ oz onion, chopped
100g/3½ oz carrots, sliced (unpeeled)
2 celery sticks, sliced
*50g/2oz green beans, in 2.5cm/1in
lengths*
*50g/2oz lean bacon, scissor-chopped
(optional)*
1tbsp olive oil, bacon or duck fat
4 garlic cloves, crushed
*390g/14oz canned kidney
(or other) beans*
100g/3½ oz ripe plum tomatoes, diced
*25g/1oz capellini (angel hair
pasta), broken*
1 vegetable stock cube, crumbled
1.5 litres/2½ pints boiling water
50g/2oz fresh parsley, chopped

Put the first 6 ingredients in a
large rigid microwave-proof bowl,
casserole or jug. Microwave,
uncovered, on HIGH for 6 minutes,
stirring halfway through.

Add the garlic, beans and their
liquid, tomatoes, pasta, stock cube
and then the boiling water, in this
order. Stir. Cover and microwave
on HIGH for 10 minutes more.
Stir again. Leave to stand for
2 minutes.

Sprinkle copiously with parsley
and serve hot in mugs, perhaps
with thin crackers or Melba toasts
for contrast.

PASTA WITH RED PEPPER & SALMON SAUCE

CALORIES PER SERVING: 236
SERVES: 6

A ravishing recipe such as this
warrants absolutely fresh nuts and
first-class smoked salmon, not just
trimmings, so taste before you buy.
Easy, deli-style food, fit for any
occasion, and with so little saturated
fat present, it's really heart-
helpful too!

VARIATIONS
1. Serve the sauce over freshly cooked
new potatoes, rather than on pasta.
2. Serve over microwave-cooked fresh
salmon, accompanied by bag-cooked
samphire and crusty rye bread.

*2 red peppers, halved lengthwise
and seeded (or 225g/8oz cooked,
skinned peppers)*
*125g/4oz smoked wild salmon,
scissor-chopped*
juice of 1 large lemon
*50g/2oz roasted salted cashew
nuts, chopped*
3 garlic cloves, crushed
*½ tsp chopped chilli
(optional)*
1tbsp extra virgin olive oil
4tbsp dry white wine, heated
*225g/8oz dry pasta: spaghettini or
capellini, broken in half*
seasalt
*50g/2oz leaves: sorrel, watercress
or nasturtium*

Put the pepper halves, skins
upmost, in a microwave roasting
bag and seal loosely. Microwave
on HIGH for 9–10 minutes or until
the flesh softens and there's an
aromatic smell. Close the bag
tightly with a rubber band and
leave to cool for 8–10 minutes.

Slide off the skins using
kitchen paper. Discard stalk and
membranes, then chop the
pepper flesh.

Put the smoked salmon into
a food processor with the lemon
juice, nuts, pepper flesh, garlic,
and chilli if used. Process briefly
to a thick paste. With the machine
running, trickle in the oil and wine
to make a thick, speckled, pink-
red purée.

Put the pasta in a large
microwave-proof casserole, at least
25cm/10in diameter, and add a
kettleful of boiling water and some
salt. Microwave, part covered, on
HIGH for 6 minutes. Stir, then cook
for a further 2 minutes. Leave to
stand for 1 minute, then drain.

Return the pasta to its hot dish
and add the sauce. Toss to coat,
then microwave on HIGH for
2 minutes if liked. Serve on some
sharp-tasting salad leaves.

CHILLI GARLIC PRAWNS

CALORIES PER SERVING: 175
SERVES: 4

A large 25cm/10in browning dish, the microwave equivalent of a frying pan, is essential for these quickly sizzled, spicy prawns with garlic, sesame and ginger. Use large, uncooked, shell-on tiger prawn tails and watch them turn from blue to scarlet – a revelation.

12 large raw shell-on prawn tails (about 350g/12oz)
5cm/2in piece of fresh root ginger, finely shredded
4–6 garlic cloves, crushed
½ fresh red or green chilli, seeded and shredded (optional)
1tbsp oil: groundnut or grapeseed
1tsp dark sesame oil
2tbsp dry sherry or dry vermouth
15g/½ oz fresh coriander leaves, torn (optional)

Holding each prawn down flat with one hand, use a sharp knife to cut horizontally through, leaving a small hinge at the centre of the curved back or near the tail. Press the prawns open into a 'butterfly' shape. Remove and discard the dark vein.

Prepare the ginger, garlic and chilli while preheating the browning dish in the microwave for 7 minutes (or according to the manufacturer's instructions). Without removing the dish, quickly add the oils, half the ginger, garlic and chilli, and all of the prawns, pressing them briefly down with a fish slice. Microwave, uncovered, on HIGH for 2 minutes.

Pour in the sherry, stir, add the remaining aromatics. Use tongs to turn the prawns over. Microwave, uncovered, on MEDIUM (50%) for a further 2 minutes. Add the herbs, stir and serve.

POPPYSEED POPCORN

A SWEET-SALT AND SEEDED COATING CAN TRANSFORM BORING OLD POPCORN INTO A SURPRISINGLY INTERESTING HIGH-FIBRE, LOW-CALORIE SNACK. THIS RECIPE MAKES A GENEROUS BOWLFUL, ENOUGH AS A LIGHT SNACK FOR FOUR. IT IS BEST EATEN THE SAME DAY.

CALORIES: 285 PER BOWL
(71 PER SERVING)
SERVES: 4

50g/2oz popping corn
2tbsp clear honey
1tbsp soy sauce
25g/1oz blue poppyseeds
2tsp seeds: celery or sesame (optional)

Put the popcorn into a large, sturdy microwave-proof casserole, 25cm/10in diameter (a Pyroceram/ Corning ware casserole is perfect). Cover and microwave on HIGH for 10 minutes or until almost all the grains have popped, shaking the dish halfway through.

Mix the honey and soy sauce. Stir quickly, then pour over the popcorn and stir to coat the pop-corn well. Add the seeds. Toss all together until evenly coated. Tip out into a serving bowl.

RIGHT: CHILLI GARLIC PRAWNS

TABBOULEH ON LETTUCE CUPS

CALORIES PER SERVING: 285
(PLUS 140 FOR EACH PITTA BREAD)
SERVES: 6

Traces of fresh herbs just aren't enough for decent tabbouleh: have lots – equal the green and the gold – and use only superb olive oil. Think of this Middle Eastern salad as a tonic! Tabbouleh makes a pleasant lunch with crisp leaves and warm pitta. Side dishes might include hummus, tomatoes with feta cheese, or labneh cheese and sliced cucumber.

350g/12oz bulgur (parboiled cracked wheat)
600ml/1 pint boiling water
freshly squeezed juice of 3 lemons
225g/8oz mixed fresh herbs: mint, flat-leaf parsley and coriander leaves, scissor-chopped
½ tsp cayenne pepper
½ tsp seasalt
4tbsp first pressing extra virgin olive oil
TO SERVE:
2 Little Gem lettuces or 1 cos lettuce
2 heads of chicory (optional)
4 wholemeal pittas (optional)

Put the bulgur in a large deep bowl and pour over the boiling water and two-thirds of the lemon juice. Stir. Leave to soak for ¾–1 hour or else refrigerate overnight.

Pour the soaked bulgur into a stainless steel or plastic sieve and press it briefly but firmly to dry it. Turn it into a bowl. Add the remaining lemon juice.

Food process or chop the mint, parsley and coriander to a juicy green paste. Add to the bulgur with the cayenne, salt and olive oil. Mix well, until evenly green. Taste and adjust seasonings.

Serve the tabbouleh in a cone or pyramid shape (press into a mould, if liked) on a large decorative platter, surrounded by edible leaves. Serve with warmed pitta breads (microwave in a cloth or basket on HIGH for 1–1½ minutes, turning over halfway), and have some ice and mineral water to hand.

SPICY COUSCOUS

TEN MINUTES AFTER YOU WALK IN THE FRONT DOOR THIS DISH CAN BE READY!
IT'S A CRIME NOT TO COOK COUSCOUS IN THE MICROWAVE, SINCE IT'S A DREAM OF EASE,
ITS TEXTURE STAYS FLUFFY AND NOTHING STICKS OR FORMS LUMPS.

CALORIES PER SERVING: 275
SERVES: 6

Many additions and variations are possible: please yourself. Great packed into mini pitta breads as finger food.

VARIATIONS
1. Serve surrounded by peeled lengths of cucumber, crisp Little Gem lettuce leaves and hollowed-out tomato halves. Shovel the couscous into the vegetables.
2. Serve inside rolled 'lavash' bread. (This flat, pliable, bubbly bread is found in some Iranian stores and supermarkets).
3. Shovel on to slightly hollowed-out French bread.

2tbsp harissa (hot chilli paste)
2tbsp tomato purée
1tsp salt
1tbsp fruity olive oil
1tsp ground turmeric
½ tsp ground cumin
125g/4oz leek or spring onions, finely shredded
750ml/1¼ pints boiling water
225g/8oz medium 'instant' couscous
225g/8oz green grapes (preferably muscat), halved
50g/2oz seedless raisins
25g/1oz sunflower seeds
25g/1oz nuts: pinenuts or broken walnut pieces

Put the first 7 ingredients, in order, in a medium-sized, microwave-proof, shallowish casserole or oval serving dish.

Add the boiling water and stir, then add the couscous and stir again. Cover and microwave on HIGH for 2 minutes.

Add the fruit (removing pips from grapes if preferred), sunflower seeds and nuts. Stir, and microwave, covered, on HIGH for a further 45–60 seconds. Serve immediately or use warm or even cold as a salad, plain or inside warm pitta breads.

YUM-YUM SUSHI

MICROWAVED RICE IS BLISSFULLY TASTY AND TROUBLE FREE SINCE THE TIMING LOOKS
AFTER ITSELF. PUDDING RICE (INSTEAD OF EXPENSIVE JAPANESE SUSHI RICE) IS USED HERE FOR AN
UNORTHODOX, FRUGAL, VEGETARIAN VERSION OF SUSHI. THE SECRET IS TO SEASON THE RICE
REALLY WELL, THEN TWIST THE WRAPPERS TIGHTLY TO FIX THE SHAPE.

CALORIES PER SERVING: 167
(FOR 4 SERVINGS)
SERVES: 4 OR 6

Long chilling seems to improve
flavours, so this is wonderful make-
ahead fare for treats or entertaining.
Don't be discouraged by the long
instructions; the recipe is easy, fun
and delicious.

*125g/4oz short-grain pudding-
type rice*
450ml/¾ pint boiling water
*2.5cm/1in piece of fresh root
ginger, shredded*
4 garlic cloves, crushed
1tbsp nam pla (fish sauce) or soy sauce
2tbsp dry sherry
1tbsp white wine vinegar
2tbsp caster sugar
4 slim red pepper strips and/or
*1 small carrot, quartered
lengthwise*
*4 French beans or slender
asparagus spears, trimmed*
4 spring onions, trimmed
4 sheets of nori seaweed
TO SERVE:
*Kikkoman soy sauce, wasabi paste,
green ginger paste or pink
pickled ginger*

Put the rice, boiling water, ginger
and garlic in a 2 litre/3½ pint
microwave-proof jug. Cover
and microwave on HIGH for
12½ minutes. Leave to stand for
5 minutes.

Add the next 4 ingredients and
stir. Leave for 5–8 minutes, to
cool. The rice should be sticky
but not wet, so drain off any
excess liquid.

Meanwhile, combine the
vegetables and 2tbsp boiling water
in a microwave-proof dish.
Microwave, uncovered, on HIGH
for 1 minute. Refresh under cold
water and drain.

Briefly 'toast' each nori sheet in
the microwave for 30 seconds on
HIGH. This helps to develop the
flavour.

Set a sheet of nori on a square of
clingfilm. Put half the rice on the
nori sheet. Pat out the rice with
wet hands until it covers all but a
5cm/2in border at the far edge of
each sheet.

Arrange horizontal lines of
stuffing ingredients left to right
across the near edge: red pepper
and/or carrot, beans or asparagus,
then spring onions.

Holding the near clingfilm
edge, tightly roll up the nori to
enclose the rice filling completely.
Go as far as the uncovered border,
then wet this and finish the rolling.
Roll a second nori sheet around
the completed sushi roll. Roll up
the 'sausage' of sushi tightly in the
clingfilm.

Twist both ends tightly like a
Christmas cracker, then secure
with rubber bands. Repeat this
entire process with the remaining
ingredients to make a second sushi
roll. Chill for at least 30 minutes
(or as long as 24 hours) in order to
develop the wonderful flavours of
the sushi.

At serving time, without
unwrapping it, slice each sushi
roll crosswise into 8 or 12 portions,
using a very sharp knife wiped
clean between each cut. Remove
and discard the clingfilm.

Arrange 4 or 6 sushi portions
on each plate, cut sides up. Set
Japanese condiments in little
dishes alongside or in the middle
of the table for everyone's use. Dip
the sushi into the spicy sauces or
seasonings, then eat.

MAIN COURSES:
HEALTHY OPTIONS

What's for supper? This daily refrain is common the world over. And where before the answer would have been a meal planned around red meat, today's healthy eaters may prefer seafood, especially fish rich in the Omega-3 oils known to be good for heart health. Other popular choices are game, naturally lean because of its habitat and lifestyle, and the white meat portions of turkey and chicken. All are low in calories and taste great. But lean, humanely reared, properly aged and well-butchered meat is still a great treat, worth paying more for and eating less often, perhaps. Be well informed and insist on the best from your butcher, fishmonger or supermarket supplier.

Each week plan on two main meals of fish, one of game, two meals of turkey or chicken, one beef, lamb, pork or veal main meal and maybe one (or more) vegetarian suppers. 'Lean-cooking' methods possible in the microwave for fish, meat and game include: baking, lean-roasting, stewing, steaming, sautéing, pan-griddling (using a preheated browning dish), cooking in paper (*en papillote*) and poaching. These are the basic essentials in this book. I have avoided high-fat techniques and calorific extras but tasty alternatives are provided.

Fish and poultry recipes predominate in this chapter. Game and pink and red meats make up the balance. Turn to the Snacks chapter and the Versatile Vegetables chapter for vegetarian alternatives. Try to serve a dark green leafy salad whenever possible, or a tomato salad or mixtures with herbs, nuts, seeds and bean sprouts perhaps. How about serving vegetables as a course in their own right? Be inventive – have you ever thought of putting pawpaw in with the lettuce? Mix fruits and vegetables and revel in foods in their due season.

If you are weight watching there are no prizes for a clean plate, so stop eating and drinking when you feel you've had enough. You'll know your own capacity better after a diet plan has been going for some time. Recognize hunger as a natural trigger and use it – don't fear it and let it sabotage your day. If your healthy appetite knows its hunger will be satisfied, then there's no reason for neurotic nibbling of factory-made snacks nor anxious, panicky eating of fat-saturated cakes, pastries and sugary sweets which damage so much more than just resolve. Finally, be in tune with your own needs. A weekend stroll or mountain hike encourage different eating patterns. The best food is most often the food you have made to suit yourself.

LEFT: MAGIC RACK OF LAMB SERVED WITH MAYAN MAIZE PURÉE WITH CHILLI; RED ONIONS *AU NATUREL*

MAGIC RACK OF LAMB

CALORIES PER SERVING: 194
SERVES: 4

This recipe requires utterly lean racks of lamb, chined, frenched and trimmed. To chine a best end, the rib bones are cut free from the backbone leaving the eye of the meat intact and the meat very easy to carve. When the thin strips of meat between the bones are removed (keep these for soup), then it is 'frenched'. Bone ends may also be shortened or trimmed. Finally, instruct your butcher to strip away every bit of surface fat or else do this final stage yourself. You will end up with two superb strips of lean muscle meat, each attached to its 7 or 8 neatly separated (frenched) 'handle' bones. Microwave cooking is superb for this – 6 minutes only to cook 2 choice succulent little joints. Truly magic!

2 racks of lamb from 'best end of neck'
(each 7–8 cutlets), sinews and
chine bone removed, bones frenched
and trimmed clean
2tsp rich soy sauce
1tsp anchovy paste or 1 canned
anchovy, chopped and mashed
1tsp honey
2tsp garlic purée
2tsp tomato purée
6tbsp robust red wine: Pinot Noir
fresh oregano, mint or rosemary
to garnish (optional)

For totally lean meat: holding a lower corner, strip away all fat cover from the meat, then use a sharp knife to free this flap from the bones. (Discard the fat, reserve meat trimmings etc.)

Wrap the scraped-clean rib bones with 2 sheets of wet kitchen paper. Mix the soy sauce, anchovy, honey, garlic purée and tomato purée together in a microwave-proof bowl or jug. Brush half of this soy glaze over

both lamb joints. Set the joints, meat outwards, evenly spaced on a grooved or pierced microwave roasting dish. Microwave, uncovered, on HIGH for 5–6 minutes, depending on your preference; halfway through, give the dish a quarter turn. Wrap the lamb in foil and leave to stand while you make the sauce.

Drain the meat juices into the remaining soy glaze and stir in the wine. Microwave, uncovered, on HIGH for 2 minutes or until aromatic and very hot. Cover and set aside. (Reheat later if necessary.)

Uncover the lamb and carve into 14–16 neat rosy cutlets. Pour all the juices into the sauce and stir.

Overlap 3–4 cutlets on each plate. Pour some of the hot sauce over and around them, garnish and serve with appropriate sweet-flavoured vegetables.

LAMB KOFTA KEBABS

CALORIES PER SERVING: 334
SERVES: 4

Lean lamb and wheat have an age-old natural affinity and, eaten together, provide good nutritional balance. These rectangular, hand-made sausages on sticks are splendidly simple to make at home and you will more than rival most local kebab houses! Microwave cooking gives lean, tender results plus a sauce. Finger food for any occasion.

4tbsp boiling water
4tbsp bulgur (parboiled cracked wheat)
450g/1lb very lean lamb, twice
minced (if possible)
1 onion, chopped
15g/½ oz fresh herbs: mint, parsley,
coriander or a mixture of these
1tsp ground cumin
1tsp coriander seeds, crushed
2tsp rich soy sauce (for glaze)
6tbsp robust red wine (for sauce)

Pour the boiling water over the bulgur and leave to soak until absorbed.

Meanwhile, put the lamb mince

into a food processor with the onion. Process in brief bursts. Add the herbs, cumin and coriander seeds together with the softened bulgur. Process again briefly until the meat forms a neat ball.

Using wet hands, pat out the meat into a rectangle about 30 × 15cm/12 × 6in on a sheet of non-stick Teflon-coated fabric or a baking sheet. Mark into 12 batons. Push a wooden kebab or satay stick down each. You now have 12 sausages on sticks. Lift using a palette knife or fish slice.

To cook 1 serving: Arrange 3 kebabs around the edge of a flat, microwave-proof plate. Microwave, uncovered, on HIGH for 2½–3 minutes; after 1½ minutes, turn them over. Pour off the juices into a microwave-proof bowl or jug and reserve. Brush soy sauce over each kebab, then wrap in foil and set aside. Microwave the lamb juices with 2tbsp wine, uncovered, on HIGH for 30–45 seconds or until bubbling. Stir, then pour over the kebabs.

To cook all 12 kebabs: Arrange 6 kebabs parallel on a microwave-proof plate. Lay the remaining 6 on top, at a right angle.

Microwave, uncovered, on HIGH for 9 minutes. After 3 minutes, turn all kebabs over, top to bottom, and reposition them (from outer to inner positions). Pour off and reserve the juices at the same time. Proceed with the soy glaze and sauce (as for single serving), but using all the wine.

Serve, perhaps, with rice, sliced tomato and cucumber, wholewheat pitta bread and my delicious recipe for American Pickles (page 117).

CELEBRATION BEEF SIRLOIN WITH BLACK OLIVES

CALORIES PER SERVING: 363
SERVES: 10

Prime Scots beef is sensational. Season it with an unusual combination of olives and garlic and serve it thinly sliced, first hot and then later cold for a subsequent meal. Microwave roasting is quick and effortless, especially for even-shaped joints such as this, though this is hardly an everyday dish, nor low in calories. Make it as an occasional treat.

NOTE: If you have a microwave with browning facilities you may wish to use them, but take care not to overcook.

SERVING SUGGESTIONS
Mashed yellow- or orange-fleshed sweet potato, celeriac or swede with some red or green cabbage would make fine accompaniments.

1 × 2.3kg/5lb piece of beef: preferably Aberdeen Angus boneless rolled sirloin
2tbsp rich soy sauce
10 garlic cloves, halved lengthwise
20 black olives, stoned
freshly ground black pepper
GRAVY:
150ml/¼ pint full-bodied red wine: Cabernet Sauvignon
1tbsp arrowroot
4tbsp single malt whisky
4tbsp water
seasalt flakes

Rub the outer surfaces of the beef with soy sauce. Push a garlic piece inside each olive. Make incisions round the circumference of the beef using a sharp, short-bladed knife, then twist the blade and insert the garlicked olives.

Put the meat, on its side, on a ridged or pierced microwave roasting dish and pepper it generously. Microwave, uncovered, on HIGH allowing 6 minutes for every 450g/1lb weight of beef. This timing (about 30 minutes) gives a rose-pink centre and a browned edge. If you insist on well-cooked beef, allow 8 minutes per 450g/1lb. (Insert a meat thermometer if in doubt after the allowed time: the internal temperature for rare beef is 51°C/125°F.)

Wrap the cooked meat in a large sheet of foil and leave to stand in a warm place until serving time, for maximum succulence.

Make the gravy by pouring off all the meat juices into a large microwave-proof jug. Add the red wine. Microwave, uncovered, on HIGH for 5–6 minutes or until aromatic and syrupy. Mix the arrowroot, whisky and water. Add to the hot gravy and microwave, uncovered, on HIGH for 1½ minutes more or until the gravy thickens and alcohol evaporates, giving a flavourful sauce. Taste, season as necessary and keep hot.

Unwrap the meat and pour the juices into the gravy. Slice the beef thinly, and serve with gravy and a little rowan or redcurrant jelly.

CITRUS PORK TENDERLOIN

CALORIES PER SERVING: 246
SERVES: 4

Neat 'coins' of lean, tender pork have an outstanding carrot, apple, orange and lemon juice glaze. Make these juices by using a 'juicer', since normal lemon squeezers cannot produce juices from non-citrus fruits. Failing this, try a juice bar or an ethnic market juice stall, and mix bought carrot and apple juices with hand-squeezed citrus ones. A fruit and vegetable juice concentrate is the last resort.

1 pork fillet (tenderloin), weighing about 450g/1lb, halved crosswise

2tsp mild paprika

1tsp rich soy sauce

1tbsp extra virgin olive oil

300ml/½ pint freshly squeezed blend of juices: apple, carrot, lemon and orange

2tsp Dijon mustard

2 garlic cloves, chopped

1tsp fécule (potato flour)

1tbsp cold water

15g/½ oz fresh parsley, chopped (optional)

Preheat a browning dish for 5 minutes. Meanwhile, evenly coat the pork fillet halves with a mixture of paprika and soy sauce.

Add the oil to the hot dish (without removing it from the microwave), then put on the 2 meat pieces, towards the back of the dish. Press them down with a fish slice for 30 seconds, then rearrange them on the front part of the dish, turning them over to sizzle the second side. Microwave, uncovered, on HIGH for 2 minutes.

Add the juices and microwave, uncovered, on MEDIUM (50%) for 5 minutes more. Remove the meat with tongs. Add the mustard and garlic and microwave the sauce for a further 2 minutes.

Slice the meat diagonally into 32–36 pieces. Replace these with any meat juices in the dish and spoon over the sauce to coat. Microwave, uncovered, on MEDIUM (50%) for 2 minutes more or until the meat looks a pale beige.

Push the meat to one side of the dish. Mix the *fécule* and water, then stir into the sauce. Microwave, uncovered, on HIGH for a final 1 minute. Serve the slices of pork, overlapped, on a pool of sauce, dusted with parsley.

PORK CHOPS ADOBO

CALORIES PER SERVING: 335
SERVES: 4

A quick, tasty Filipino dish adapted from one I learned working alongside Madhur Jaffrey. The pork has a strong 'pickled' flavour, and rather than the traditional fatty belly pork, I use lean, well-trimmed boneless pork loin chops. Delicious with rice, beans and soft buns to scoop up the extra sauce.

500g/1lb 2oz boneless lean pork chops (about 4–5)

4tbsp dark soy sauce

4tbsp distilled malt vinegar

4 garlic cloves, crushed

6 star anise pods

8 large spring onions, halved crosswise

300ml/½ pint boiling stock or water

3tbsp dry sherry

3tbsp arrowroot

3tbsp cold water

Arrange the pork in a shallow microwave-proof casserole in one layer. Add the soy sauce, vinegar, garlic, star anise and the white portions of the spring onions (reserve green tops for later). Add the boiling stock or water. Cover and microwave on HIGH for 8 minutes or until very hot. Turn the meat over with tongs and cover again. Microwave on MEDIUM (50%) for 8 minutes more. Remove the meat from the sauce.

Reduce the sticky sauce by microwaving, uncovered, on HIGH for 6 minutes; after 5 minutes, add the sherry. Add the arrowroot and water, mixed, and stir. Microwave on HIGH for a final minute.

Replace the pork in the hot sauce. Scatter with green spring onion shreds and serve hot.

TRIMPORK BOLOGNESE

THIS RECIPE FOLLOWS A VAGUE BOLOGNESE FORMULA BUT USES EXTRA-LEAN PORK, WITH CHICKEN LIVERS, LEMON AND SAGE AS FLAVOURINGS. THERE'S NO BROWNING IN ADDED OIL (IN FACT ALL OIL AND JUICES ARE DRAINED OFF) AND THE ACCOMPANYING FRESH PASTA HAS A LEMONY-CHEESY COATING. A FUTURE MICROWAVE WEEKLY FAVOURITE PERHAPS?

CALORIES PER SERVING: 261
SERVES: 6

SAUCE:
*450g/1lb lean pork, minced
(less than 10% fat)*
2 red onions, chopped
4 garlic cloves, crushed
*100g/3½ oz chicken livers,
scissor-chopped*
6 ripe, red plum tomatoes, sliced
3tbsp rich soy sauce
2tbsp tomato purée
*2tbsp sun-dried tomato paste or
6 sun-dried tomatoes, chopped*
*4 anchovies, scissor-chopped, or
1tbsp anchovy paste*
*½ tsp chopped fresh sage (or half
that volume dried)*

PASTA:
grated zest and juice of 2 lemons
225g/8oz fresh spaghetti
salt
*100g/3½ oz low-fat soft cheese or
ricotta*
freshly ground black pepper

Put the pork mince in a microwave-proof pasta basket (inside a microwave-proof bowl) or in a pierced microwave-proof steamer. Microwave, uncovered, on HIGH for 5 minutes. Break up the meat into small clumps. Drain off all fat and juice and reserve for other uses (e.g. in soups or with vegetables).

Put the onions, garlic and half the lemon juice in a microwave-proof ring dish. Microwave, uncovered, on HIGH for 5 minutes, stirring halfway through. Add the cooked pork and the chopped livers, then stir in all the remaining sauce ingredients. Microwave, uncovered, on HIGH for 10 minutes; halfway through, stir the mixture and give the dish a quarter turn. Add half the lemon zest, stir and leave to stand, covered, while the pasta cooks.

Put the spaghetti in a large microwave-proof pasta basket inside a microwave-proof bowl, or put directly into a large microwave-proof casserole. Pour over a generous kettleful of water and add salt to taste. Microwave, part-covered, on HIGH for 5 minutes or until bite-tender. Drain.

Return the pasta to its still-hot bowl (without the basket) and add the remaining lemon zest and juice and the soft cheese mashed to a paste. Toss to coat. Leave to stand while the meat sauce briefly reheats (2 minutes), uncovered, on HIGH.

Serve the spaghetti on a large flat platter and top with pepper. Pour the sauce on top and garnish with, perhaps, some herbs. Green pepper and rocket salad, crusty bread and some good red wine would not be unwelcome.

CHICKEN SANTA CRUZ

CALORIES PER SERVING: 181
SERVES: 6

A Mayan chicken dish from Guatemala with several different tastes that blend surprisingly well. One odd but authentic addition is Worcestershire sauce, which arrived via visiting sailors a century ago. If preferred, marinate the chicken some time ahead for stronger flavour though the briefer timing works splendidly. Rice or black beans plus a watercress salad would taste just fine.

6 chicken supremes, total weight
675g/1½ lb
1tbsp Worcestershire sauce
3tbsp freshly squeezed
lime juice
2tbsp corn oil
1 large onion, sliced
3–4 ripe tomatoes, cubed
½ tsp salt
1–2tsp chilli powder

Put the poultry in a shallow non-metal dish. Pierce it all over using a fork. Mix the Worcestershire sauce and lime juice together. Rub them well into the chicken, pouring over any extra. Leave to stand while the vegetables are prepared, or longer (up to 24 hours).

Preheat a browning dish in the microwave for 6 minutes (or according to manufacturer's instructions). Without removing the dish from the microwave, quickly add the oil, onion and drained chicken portions, curved sides down. Allow to sizzle for 30–40 seconds or so.

Use tongs to turn the chicken over. Add the tomatoes, salt, chilli and any remaining marinade. Microwave, covered, on HIGH for 8 minutes; halfway through, shake the pan and give it a quarter turn, but do not uncover it – the steam helps the chicken cook even more effectively. Serve hot.

CHICKEN MISHMISH

MISHMISH IS ARABIC FOR APRICOT, AND WHAT'S NEEDED IS THE BRIGHT-COLOURED, DRY, SHARP-TASTING, OLD-FASHIONED KIND, NOT THE READY-TO-EAT PRE-SOAKED BRANDS WITH LESS BITE. THIS ALL-IN-ONE DISH, WITH ITS COPIOUS GOLDEN SAUCE, IS CHILD'S PLAY BUT SUPERB FOR HEALTHY MEALS AND ENTERTAINING TOO.

CALORIES PER SERVING: 299
SERVES: 4

NOTE: If wished, drain the chicken and vegetables and keep hot while you reduce the liquid: microwave, uncovered, on high for 12–15 minutes until very thick.

SERVING SUGGESTIONS
Baby Potatoes *en Papillote* with Wine & Mint (page 85) and Green Beans with Garlic *en Papillote* (page 88) or a green salad make good accompaniments.

6 chicken thighs, skinned and
boned
6 large chicken wings
300ml/½ pint freshly squeezed
orange juice
150ml/¼ pint fresh apple juice
freshly squeezed juice of 1 lemon
2 medium onions, halved and sliced
5cm/2in piece of fresh root ginger,
shredded
16 dried apricot halves, half of them
scissor-chopped
1tsp light soy sauce
pinch of cayenne pepper
pinch of powdered saffron
2tbsp toasted sesame seeds

Flatten the chicken pieces as much as possible. Combine them with all the other ingredients (except for the sesame seeds) in a microwave-proof casserole, 25cm/10in in diameter and about 2.6 litre/4½ pint volume. Cover with a lid and cook on HIGH for 10 minutes.

Uncover and use tongs to turn the chicken pieces over, repositioning them from the edges to the centre.

Cover again. Microwave on MEDIUM (50%) for a further 30 minutes or until the chicken is fork-tender and the sauce slightly syrupy. Leave to stand, covered, for 2 minutes.

Serve sprinkled with some toasted sesame seeds.

CHICKEN MISHMISH SERVED WITH GREEN BEANS WITH GARLIC; BABY POTATOES *EN PAPILLOTE* WITH WINE & MINT

SINGAPORE CHICKEN IN ITS BROTH

THIS SIMPLE TECHNIQUE, TAUGHT TO ME BY MY HOST WHILE HOLIDAYING IN SINGAPORE,
ENSURES TENDER, AROMATIC CHICKEN AND A DELICATE FRAGRANT BROTH TO BE SERVED BEFORE,
WITH OR AFTER THE BIRD.

CALORIES PER SERVING: 230
SERVES: 6

Though the bay and thyme seem excessive they work well in this cross-cultural recipe. Search out a first-class, fresh not frozen, free-range bird, ideally with giblets, from a reliable supplier, and the Szechuan pepper from an Oriental supplier.

1 tbsp Szechuan pepper
*1 × 1.5 kg/3¼ lb corn-fed,
free-range chicken*
*1 large sprig of fresh bay
(10–12 leaves), lightly crushed*
50g/2oz fresh thyme, tied with string
1 small red pepper, seeded and sliced
*1 leek, halved crosswise and then
quartered lengthwise, green top
rinsed and reserved*
1 onion, quartered
*2.5cm/1in piece of fresh root
ginger, crushed*
1 large fresh chilli, split and seeded
*1.1 litres/2 pints boiling water
(or more depending on pan size)*
1 tbsp soy sauce
seasalt flakes
4 spring onions

Scatter the Szechuan pepper on a microwave-proof plate. Microwave, uncovered, on HIGH for 1 minute or until toasted and aromatic. Pound, crush or grind to reduce to a powder.

Use a cleaver or poultry shears to halve the bird down its length. Pat dry inside and out with kitchen paper. Rub the Szechuan pepper over the inside surfaces. Scissor-chop the giblets.

Put the bird halves, overlapped, skin side up, in a large deep microwave-proof bowl or casserole, about 25cm/10in in diameter. Add the giblets, bay, thyme, red pepper, the white part of the leek, onion, ginger and chilli. Cover the chicken, vegetables and herbs with the boiling water.

Cover with pierced microwave-proof clingfilm or a lid. Microwave on HIGH for 30 minutes. Give the

dish a quarter turn and then microwave on HIGH for 20 minutes more or until very aromatic. Add the soy sauce, green leek top and 1 tbsp seasalt flakes. Cover again and microwave on HIGH for a final 10 minutes.

Leave to stand for 5 minutes, then seal tightly using clingfilm and cover with a folded cloth. Leave absolutely undisturbed (not even one glimpse) for 8 hours or overnight.

Lift out the chicken (which will still be warm) and tip to drain the halves; set aside. Strain the broth through a sieve set in a bowl. Discard all solids except the heart and liver. Drag torn sheets of kitchen paper across the surface of the broth several times to absorb floating fat. Taste the broth and season if necessary, but take care not to overpower the delicate taste.

Pull away the chicken skin and discard it. Carefully strip all meat from the bones, discarding the debris. Arrange the lean, skinless chicken in a shallow microwave-proof serving dish. Pour in sufficient stock just to cover it – about 450ml/¾ pint. Chop the whites of the spring onions into fine rounds and shred the greens lengthwise; scatter on top. Microwave, covered, on HIGH for 4–6 minutes or until very hot.

Serve in bowls, with separate bowls of noodles and Chinese greens. Serve the remaining broth steaming hot as an extra or freeze in ice trays for future cooking.

LEMON GRASS CHICKEN

CALORIES PER SERVING: 200
SERVES: 4

Cooked garlic, tea and Oriental herbs create a sweet, delicately scented, thin sauce. Lemon grass (available at Far Eastern grocers and some supermarkets) ideally should be green and fresh. If dried is the only alternative then strain the sauce through a sieve after blending it.

SERVING SUGGESTIONS
Serve with well-seasoned brown rice, noodles or flat breads and a cucumber salad or some aubergine (cooked *au naturel*, page 81) dressed with sesame oil and sesame seeds.

2tbsp grapeseed oil
1 head of garlic, separated into cloves, peeled and pricked
2 heads of fresh lemon grass, quartered lengthwise
4 chicken breast portions (about 450g/1lb), skinned and boned
1 small green birdseye chilli, seeded and slashed
300ml/½ pint freshly made Earl Grey tea
1tsp light soy sauce
15g/½ oz fresh coriander leaves

Preheat a browning dish in the microwave for 6 minutes (or according to the manufacturer's instructions). Without removing it, add the oil, garlic cloves, lemon grass and chicken to the dish, pressing the breasts down with a fish slice on to the sizzling pan. Microwave, uncovered, on HIGH for 3 minutes.

Add the chilli, tea, soy sauce and most of the coriander. Turn the chicken breasts over, outer edges towards the centre. Cover and microwave on HIGH for 6 minutes more. (The chicken should feel firm.)

Remove the chicken and lemon grass. Use a blender to purée the sauce, adding the reserved coriander leaves. Slice each chicken breast lengthwise into 9–10 thin strips. Arrange in a fan shape on a share of lemon grass and trickle over the hot sauce.

POULTRY BROCHETTES WITH PRUNES & CALVADOS

CALORIES PER SERVING: 309
SERVES: 4

Brochettes such as these with such lean meat and gutsy flavours, boosted by strong liquor and fennel seeds, become a treat for any season, from summery parties to autumnal suppers. It is always best to use a corn-fed chicken or a free-range turkey and to allow the meat to marinate for 15 minutes if possible.

SERVING SUGGESTIONS
Serve 4 brochettes per person, with Kibbled Wheat with Herbs *en Papillote* (page 89) and a dandelion leaf and raw spinach salad. I prefer to arrange the brochettes as follows: poultry, stuffed prune, pepper, poultry, pepper, spring onion, pepper.

450g/1lb turkey or corn-fed chicken breast meat, skinned
16 stoned ready-to-eat prunes
4tbsp brandy: marc, calvados or cognac
2 garlic cloves, crushed
½ tsp Chinese 5-spice powder
2tsp fennel seeds
2tbsp soy sauce
4 spring onions
85g/3oz low-fat soft cheese
2 yellow peppers, seeded, each cut into 24 pieces
3tbsp apricot jam

Cut the meat into 32 neat cubes. Put these, the prunes, brandy, garlic, 5-spice powder, fennel seeds and soy sauce in a plastic bag. Close tightly and knead the bag a little. Cut the spring onions into quarter lengths. Divide the soft cheese into 16 equal pieces.

Drain the prunes, push some cheese inside each one and close the edges again. Remove the poultry from its bag, reserving the marinade. Assemble 16 brochettes, using thick wooden skewers about 20cm/8in long. Combine the jam and reserved marinade in a microwave-proof jug. Microwave, uncovered, on HIGH for 1½ minutes, stirring halfway through.

Arrange 8 brochettes in a ring around the edge of a large, oiled, microwave-proof platter (avoiding overlap if possible). Brush with the marinade. Microwave, uncovered, on HIGH for 2 minutes. Turn the brochettes over, rearranging them head to tail, and microwave for a further 3 minutes. Foil-wrap and leave to stand while the remaining 8 brochettes are cooked.

VENISON SALAD; POULTRY BROCHETTES WITH PRUNES & CALVADOS

VENISON SALAD

CALORIES PER SERVING: 139
SERVES: 4

Since venison is very lean indeed, it should be kept succulent by rapid cooking, so needs to be well seasoned first. Here, using barely a film of oil in the pan, a luscious, simple sauce complements the rare meat. A simply stunning dish accomplished in under 15 minutes.

SERVING SUGGESTION
Serve with separate dishes of sweet potato purée and skinned, peppered and salted tamarillo slices, if liked.

VARIATION
Well trimmed beef sirloin or rump could be substituted for venison.

2 × 175g/6oz venison haunch
steaks
seasalt flakes
15g/½ oz fresh thyme sprigs
1tsp virgin olive oil
2tbsp grainy mustard
6tbsp full-bodied red wine
2tbsp virtually-no-fat fromage frais
225g/8oz mixed red and green
salad leaves

Season the well-dried venison with salt and crushed thyme leaves. Preheat a browning dish in the microwave until very hot (about 8 minutes). Add the oil and then the steaks. Press down with a fish slice for 10 seconds; do not turn

the steaks over. Sizzle the steaks, uncovered, on HIGH for 1½ minutes; halfway through, turn the meat over with tongs and give the dish a quarter turn. Stack and foil-wrap the steaks to keep hot.

Stir the mustard and red wine in the browning dish. Microwave, uncovered, on HIGH for about 1½ minutes or until slightly reduced and syrupy. Add the fromage frais, stir and microwave on HIGH for 30 seconds more.

Slice the venison thinly into strips and arrange on the mixed salad leaves. Spoon the meat juices and sauce over and serve.

BLANQUETTE DE VEAU

CALORIES PER SERVING: 240
SERVES: 6

Delicate unbrowned veal bathed in a pearly sauce flavoured with dried ceps is a little unorthodox but results in a deliciously lean stew. Initial fast cooking then gentler stewing and thickening of the sauce are achieved really easily thanks to the microwave controls.

SERVING SUGGESTIONS
Plain boiled rice is the classic accompaniment along with crusty French bread. Garnish the dish with parsley if desired and follow with a green bean salad.

1kg/2.2lb stewing veal: breast,
in 5cm/2in squares
8g/¼ oz dried ceps
2 carrots, halved lengthwise
1 onion, quartered
4 garlic cloves, crushed
20 black peppercorns
1 bouquet garni
450ml/¾ pint boiling water
150ml/¾ pint dry white wine
3 egg yolks
1tbsp fécule (potato starch)
4tbsp virtually-no-fat fromage frais
seasalt flakes
1tbsp freshly squeezed lemon juice

Pierce each piece of veal with a fork and put into a 25cm/10in diameter casserole. Add the dried mushrooms, vegetables, garlic, peppercorns and bouquet garni. Cover with the boiling water. Microwave, uncovered, on HIGH for 18 minutes; halfway through,

turn the veal pieces over and rearrange them, edges to centre, and give the dish a quarter turn.

Add the wine. Microwave, uncovered, on LOW (30%) for 30 minutes longer ; halfway through, rearrange the veal and give the dish a quarter turn. Discard the bouquet garni. Remove the meat and vegetables and keep hot in a serving dish. Microwave the stock on HIGH, uncovered, for 5 minutes until slightly reduced and very hot.

Whisk together the egg yolks, *fécule* and fromage frais. Ladle in some hot stock. Whisk, then return to the casserole. Stir to mix. Microwave, uncovered, on MEDIUM (50%) for 2 minutes more, then 1 extra minute on HIGH. Taste and season, then add the lemon juice. Pour the sauce over the meat and vegetables and serve.

Quail in Red Vermouth

THESE SUCCULENT LITTLE BIRDS WITH THEIR ROSY PINK ACCOMPANIMENTS
ARE SIMPLICITY ITSELF TO COOK. (USE THE BONELESS VERSION FOR PARTIES –
A REAL DELIGHT TO EAT.) MICROWAVE-COOKING KEEPS QUAIL
TENDER AND SWEET. GREAT WEEKEND OR PICNIC FARE, BUT PROVIDE BIG NAPKINS.

CALORIES PER SERVING: 344
SERVES: 4

*8 oven-ready quail
(or boned quail)*
2tsp olive oil
freshly ground black pepper
*4 thin slices cured ham,
eg Jambon de Bayonne, halved*
*8 large outer radicchio leaves plus
8 additional leaves*
1tbsp strawberry vinegar
150ml/¼ pint red vermouth
*225g/8oz black grapes, halved
and seeded*
handful of fresh chervil (optional)

Oil and pepper each bird, then
wrap neatly in a half slice of ham,
securing with a wooden cocktail
stick beneath. Pierce the breasts
(through the ham) and legs of the
birds in several places, using a
cocktail stick. Enclose each bird
in a large radicchio leaf.

Arrange the birds evenly
around the edge of a 23cm/9in
ring dish (2 litres/3½ pints
capacity). Mix the vinegar and
vermouth and pour over, along
with three-quarters of the grapes.

Microwave, clingfilm covered,
on HIGH for 24 minutes, giving the
dish a half turn halfway through
the cooking. Remove the birds to a
serving dish, cover and keep hot.

Reduce the sauce: microwave,
uncovered, on HIGH for 5–7
minutes, until the liquid becomes
syrupy, tilting the dish
occasionally to mix the juices.

Spoon the hot sauce over the
cooked quail. Garnish with
additional raw, brightly coloured
leaves, the remaining grapes and
the fresh chervil. If liked, allow
the birds to cool, then chill and
serve cold.

BASIC FISH RECIPE

SUITABLE FISH: Trout, salmon, sea bass, halibut, turbot, parrot fish, sole, flounder, mullet, plaice, cod, haddock, whiting, snapper, bream, hake, arctic char, herring, mackerel, huss, skate, hoki.

NOTE: Swordfish and tuna, because of their dense structure, may need shorter cooking times but extra 'cook-on' time to compensate. Marinating suits them both well.

4 × 125–175g/4–6oz fish fillet portions: cutlets or steaks
½ lemon
salt and freshly ground black pepper
1tsp chopped fresh herbs

Set the fish, arranged like the spokes of a wheel, with thinner ends pointed towards the centre, around the edge of a microwave-proof serving plate or casserole. Squeeze the lemon juice over. Cover loosely, using greaseproof paper, clingfilm or a lid.

Microwave on HIGH for 2, 3 or 4 minutes, then test the fillets for doneness. If necessary cook for an extra minute. Season and add fresh herbs. Serve with appropriate accompaniments: wedges of citrus fruit; fresh herbs; mango salsa; low-fat, low-calorie yogurt emulsion sauces; fresh tomato relishes; grainy mustard; herb vinaigrette; balsamic vinegar; tamarind soured chutneys; horseradish sauce; or tahini-based lemony dressings.

FOOLPROOF FISH FILLETS

FISH COOKS LIKE A DREAM IN THE MICROWAVE. IT'S DIFFICULT TO RUIN AND, SINCE THE TIMER TURNS IT OFF, THERE IS MUCH LESS CHANCE OF OVER-COOKING IT. MICROWAVED FISH, HOWEVER, DOESN'T ALWAYS FLAKE IN THE WAY TRADITIONALLY COOKED FISH DOES. TEST IT WITH THE POINT OF A KNIFE NEAR THE CENTRE: HOT AND OPAQUE AND IT'S READY.

CALORIES PER SERVING: 135 (175G/6OZ COD FILLET EACH)
SERVES: 4

Symmetrical shapes cook best, so protect small thin areas with foil (but never in contact with the top, base or sides of microwave – see Safe and Efficient Microwave Use, page 9).

Microwave-stew by cooking in a sauce based on tomatoes and peppers; coconut milk and green or red curry paste; soured cream and herbs; mustardy béchamel; creamy root vegetable purée; fresh green herb salsa; or onion or cucumber pickles. All can also be used as the stewing medium, perhaps with a splash of wine or stock.

Allow 125–175g/4–6oz per serving – or more if there is much bone, skin and waste. If the fish is thickly cut and/or dense, slash skin at edges. Piercing skin with a skewer is always helpful.

For 500–675g/1lb 2oz–1½ lb allow, on average, 2, 3 or 4 minutes on HIGH. (Thinner, more delicate fish cooks quicker than thicker, denser fish.) You can always give it an extra minute or two.

For really dense fish (swordfish, tuna, monkfish) it's best to slash the flesh at the edges and also undercook, then leave to stand, covered, for 2 minutes to allow a gentle 'cook-on' effect. Otherwise, edges may toughen and overcook.

Season *after* cooking: it is often unnecessary anyway with fish.

Microwave-poach by setting fillets in 2–3tbsp of stock, wine, skimmed milk or sauce. Cover and cook.

Microwave-bake uncovered, adding a trickle or two of extra virgin olive oil, small dots of creamed coconut or of butter.

Microwave-steam by covering fish with a lid, banana leaf wrapper, baking parchment or microwave-safe clingfilm. Fish cooks in its own juices. (Optional: add some aromatics such as ginger, garlic, peppercorns, lemon grass, kaffir lime leaves.)

Microwave-'blacken' by rubbing fillets with Cajun-type spice mix. Sear it briefly in a preheated browning dish – almost no extra cooking time is needed.

FISH IN PAPER

SALMON KEBABS WITH SALSA

CALORIES PER SERVING: 358
SERVES: 4

Salmon cooked without added saturated fats is a truly tasty heart-healthy food. Here the Caribbean-style salsa acts as both marinade and sauce in a really easy but glamorous dish, as good for entertaining as it is for everyday use.

SERVING SUGGESTION
Rice, crunchy salad greens with pawpaw and mangetouts.

675g/1½ lb salmon fillets or steaks
2 red peppers
freshly squeezed juice of 2 limes
6tbsp freshly squeezed orange juice
½ bunch of spring onions,
finely chopped
¼ tsp dried crushed chillies
3tbsp extra virgin olive oil
15g/½ oz fresh coriander and/or
parsley, chopped, to garnish

Slice or scissor-cut the salmon into 32 roughly even cubes, discarding skin and bone. Dice the flesh (discarding stalks, seeds and membranes) of 1½ peppers to give 40 pieces; reserve the remaining pepper.

Finely chop the remaining red pepper flesh into tiny pieces. Add all the remaining ingredients apart from the fresh herbs, to make a salsa (sauce).

Push the salmon and pepper pieces alternately on to eight 15cm/6in wooden skewers or satay sticks, starting and finishing with pepper. Marinate the kebabs in about one-third of the salsa for 10 minutes, turning them over halfway through.

Set the kebabs around the edge of a large flat microwave-proof platter. Cover with a sheet of baking parchment.

Microwave on HIGH for 2 minutes. Turn the kebabs over and give the platter a quarter turn. Cook for a further 1 minute. (If preferred, cook a little longer: 3 minutes and 2 minutes for a firm, well-cooked result.)

Serve with the remaining salsa spooned over, and sprinkled with the fresh herbs.

FISH IN PAPER

ANY FISH COOKED IN PAPER HAS A SPECIAL CHARM BUT RED MULLET IS
EXCEPTIONAL. THIS MICROWAVE VERSION IS REVOLUTIONARY FOR FRESHNESS OF TASTE,
SPEED AND UNDIMMED COLOUR.

CALORIES PER SERVING: 144
SERVES: 4

VARIATIONS
1. Substitute 4 × 125g/4oz portions of salmon or arctic char fillet, skinned.
2. Substitute 4 × 125g/4oz portions of cod, whiting or haddock fillet, skinned. Use red peppers and orange juice, adding some hot paprika or Piri-Piri seasoning.
3. Substitute 4 × 125g/4oz portions of smoked Finnan Haddock or Arbroath Smokies fillet, with lemon juice, soured cream, sliced spring onions and black peppercorns.
4. Substitute 4 × 125g/4oz double-folded fillets of sole, flounder or plaice, with flat-leaf parsley sprigs, lemon juice, butter and white peppercorns.

4 large or 8 smaller red mullet fillets
(about 450g/1lb), scaled
85g/3oz red or orange pepper, seeded
and sliced
1 red onion, finely sliced
2tsp vinegar: raspberry or red wine
1tsp first-pressing virgin olive oil
1tbsp crushed peppercorns:
black or pink

Place a fillet skin side up on each of four 32cm/13in rectangles of baking parchment. Arrange some pepper and onion slices on each fillet, then sprinkle over some vinegar, a little oil and several peppercorns. Put the remaining fillets on top, skin side up, and repeat the seasoning process.

Bring opposite paper edges together (as for a parcel), fold over several times, then twist the other ends firmly and neatly underneath the fish. Repeat the process with each parcel.

Arrange the parcels evenly around the edge of a microwave-proof platter. Microwave on HIGH for 3½–4 minutes. Unwrap at the table and savour the wonderful sea-fresh smells.

COURGETTE-TOPPED FILLETS

A BRILLIANTLY GREEN AND BLACK SPECKLED TOPPING FOR FISH LOOKS AND TASTES
ITS ABSOLUTE BEST WHEN MICROWAVE COOKED. NOT ONLY IS THIS EASY AND INTERESTING
BUT IT IS VERY LOW IN CALORIES TOO. A TREAT!

CALORIES PER SERVING: 251
SERVES: 4

SERVING SUGGESTION
Carrot strips, potato salad and
granary bread.

*4 × 125g/4oz skinless fish fillet
portions: salmon, sea-trout, trout,
mackerel, mullet, sea bass, hoki
100g/3½ oz courgettes, finely
grated
15g/½ oz fresh Parmesan cheese,
finely grated
1tsp black onion seeds (nigella)
8g/¼ oz fresh parsley, scissor-cut
¼ tsp salt
freshly ground pepper*

TO GARNISH:
*extra parsley and lemon twists,
slices or wedges (optional)*

Place the fillets, skinned side
down, around the edges of a
microwave-proof platter. Finely
grate the unpeeled courgette by
hand or in a food processor.
Squeeze completely dry in a non-
metal sieve. Add the cheese, seeds,
parsley and salt and pepper.
Mix well. Spread some topping
over each fillet. Pat on firmly.

Microwave, uncovered, on
HIGH for 3½ minutes, or until the
topping smells aromatic and the
fish is set. Leave to stand for
1 minute, then lift off using a fish
slice so the topping is not
disturbed. Garnish with herbs and
lemon as wished.

SMOKED MACKEREL ST CLEMENT'S

SIMPLICITY ITSELF: ORANGES AND LEMONS ARE ALL YOU NEED AND SMOKED MACKEREL
(AN OILY BUT VERY HEART-HEALTHY FISH) BECOMES A HOT MAIN-COURSE DISH.
EVEN LEARNERS AND 'NON-COOKS' CAN EXCEL WITH THIS FAILPROOF RECIPE. CHILLED
AND FLAKED, THE FISH PLUS SAUCE GOES VERY WELL WITH SALAD.

CALORIES PER SERVING: 304
SERVES: 4

SERVING SUGGESTION
Potato Wedges *au Naturel* (page 83),
small crisp lettuce hearts and watercress
are suitable accompaniments.

*4 large smoked, peppered
mackerel fillets (about 550g/1¼ lb)
2 lemons
2 oranges
fresh herb sprigs:
flat-leaf parsley*

Place the mackerel fillets, skin side
down, in a shallow rectangular
microwave-proof dish big enough
to take them in one layer. Halve
and squeeze both lemons, but only
1 orange. Pour the juices evenly
over the fish.

Shred the zest of the remaining
orange using a zester or fine grater
and scatter over the top. Discard
the pith and cut the flesh into
semi-circles for garnishing.

Microwave the fish, uncovered,
on HIGH for 7–8 minutes or until
very hot and aromatic; halfway
through, turn the fillets over and
give the dish a quarter turn.

Arrange the fish flesh up, spoon
over the sauce and garnish with
sliced orange and herbs.

BILLE'S PICKLED HERRINGS

MY BERGEN-BORN FRIEND BILLE PREPARES SUPERB PICKLED HERRINGS. THEY MAKE YOU
REALIZE YOU'LL NEVER EAT COMMERCIALLY PREPARED HERRINGS AGAIN! INSTEAD OF SOURED
CREAM, I USE LOW-FAT FROMAGE FRAIS. FRESH CHIVES, CUT AT THE TABLE, ARE THE FINAL
FLOURISH FOR THIS OMEGA-3 RICH DISH.

CALORIES PER SERVING: 357
SERVES: 6

SERVING SUGGESTION
Dark rye bread and iced aquavit
are traditional Scandinavian
accompaniments.

6 × 175g/6oz herrings,
absolutely fresh
1tbsp fine seasalt
300ml/½ pint distilled malt vinegar
300ml/½ pint dry white wine:
Muscadet
2tbsp caster sugar
32 black peppercorns
20 cloves
4 fresh bay leaves, crushed
1 medium carrot, sliced
1 onion, skinned and sliced

TO SERVE:
virtually-no-fat fromage frais
50g/2oz bunch of fresh chives

Have the fishmonger scale, gut,
clean and fillet the herrings to give
12 single fillets; or do this yourself.
Trim off fins and tweezer away
tiny bones. Dry the prepared fillets
on kitchen paper. Put them in two
layers, skins down, in a non-metal
dish and sprinkle with the salt.
Refrigerate.

Combine the vinegar, wine,
sugar, peppercorns, cloves and
bay leaves in a non-metal
microwave-proof jug. Microwave,
covered, on HIGH for 8 minutes or
until boiling. Stir, cover and leave
until completely cold. (Do not be
tempted to add the fillets when it is
hot or even warm.)

Rinse the fish briefly under cold
water and pat well dry. Put several
carrot and onion slices and a bay
leaf on the bottom of an oval
earthenware terrine. Drain and
add about a quarter share of the
cloves and peppercorns. Cover
with 3 of the fillets, skins upward.
Continue this process until all the
solids are used up. Pour over
enough of the pickle liquid just to
cover the fish. Put a lid on the
terrine and refrigerate (or store in
a cool place) for 36–48 hours.
Tastes improve for up to 1 week,
so leave as long as it suits you.

Serve the drained fillets with
fromage frais and fresh chives
(have scissors at the table).

VERSATILE VEGETABLES:
GREENS, GRAINS & BEANS

Main-course protein with a drab pile of over-boiled vegetables alongside is passé. Vegetables, long-time Cinderellas of the Western kitchen, are now stars. We have grown fascinated by their versatility and are grateful that they do us so much good. These days more of us are able to travel abroad and so taste ethnic dishes that we can re-create at home. Glorious vegetables are good enough to be eaten alone. Separate your meals into components so that your family can eat according to their different appetites and timetables. Microwave cooking means that not everything needs to be hot at once or served at the same time.

The following recipes contain many familiar foods. What has been done to them, however, is not so familiar: rice combined with chayote and a hint of coconut cream, or with wine and saffron, for example. Carrots with pumpkinseed oil, salad dressed with a tamarillo and olive oil vinaigrette, sweetcorn grated and cooked as a purée, Central American style. This is variety! Some less well-known foods – turtle beans, wild rice, brown lentils and barley – become gourmet fare fit for the most elegant table. Microwave cooking keeps in the colour, the texture, the vitamins and the taste. Speed, convenience and maximized flavours are the bonuses you gain.

Nearly all root vegetables (and tubers), apart from potatoes, can be eaten raw. Many of them taste best finely shredded with a squeeze of lemon, a little seasoning and yogurt, dressing or oil to enliven the taste. Some of the dishes in this chapter can become wonderful warm salad-starters, so use them in this way to enliven your meals.

Cooking 'in a bag' is a useful method for diced, cut or small items – especially those that have a sauce, juice or dressing as an integral part of the dish. Vegetables cooked in this way retain more of their valuable nutrients. Always set the oven bag on a flat dish for easy removal once the food is cooked and super-hot. Repositioning is done by holding two corners and jiggling them to turn the contents over. Tipping the bag over also works, but use oven gloves or tongs until you are well-practised with this method. Bags can also be (machine) washed and reused, and must be sealed loosely with a plastic tie, rubber band or string, leaving a finger-sized vent to prevent steam from splitting the bag. Banana and vine leaves, Swiss chard and other leaves may also be used as cooking vessels, fastened with wooden cocktail sticks.

LEFT: CORN-ON-THE-COB *AU NATUREL*

CORN-ON-THE-COB *AU NATUREL*

THIS METHOD REVOLUTIONIZES THE TASTE OF FRESH SWEETCORN:
THE KERNELS STEAM IN THEIR OWN JUICES. SUPERB! YOU MAY FIND THAT YOU CAN DO AWAY
WITH THE USUAL PORTION OF BUTTER ON YOUR CORN WITH THIS METHOD.

CALORIES PER SERVING: 110
SERVES: 4

NOTES: For 2 cobs, allow 5–6 minutes.
For 1 cob, allow 2½–3 minutes.

4 whole fresh corncobs, silk and green husk intact
seasalt and freshly ground black pepper

Snap off any stalks. Wash the cobs, allowing a little water between husks and kernels. Arrange in a ring on a sheet of kitchen paper on a microwave-proof plate. Cover loosely with another sheet of paper.

Microwave on HIGH for 8–9 minutes; halfway through, turn the cobs over and reposition them (tip to base).

Leave to stand in the microwave for 1 minute. Pull open the husks, season and eat hot.

ASPARAGUS *AU NATUREL*

THESE ASPARAGUS SPEARS LOOK TO ME LIKE GREEN PENCILS. THE CUTTING EVENS UP
THE COOKING AT BOTH ENDS. NO EXCUSES NOW FOR NOT SERVING ASPARAGUS ALL THROUGH
SPRING OR WHENEVER YOU FIND LOVELY IMPORTED BUNCHES IN THE MARKET.

CALORIES PER SERVING: 73
SERVES: 4

NOTES: For 450g/1lb asparagus, allow 4½–5 minutes.

For particularly large or small spears, vary the cooking time accordingly by 1 minute more or less.

350g/12oz fresh green asparagus spears
25g/1oz salted butter (optional)
juice of ½ lemon
freshly ground black pepper

Snap off and discard the tough 2.5–5cm/1–2in portion at the base of each spear. Sharpen these bases, like pencils, to a 2.5cm/1in tapering point. (Shavings and tough ends, shredded, make good soup.)

Alternating tips and bases, arrange on a round or rectangular platter big enough to take all spears in one layer. Add 1tbsp water and cover with pierced microwave-safe clingfilm.

Microwave on HIGH for 3½–4 minutes, then leave to stand for 2 minutes. Part-uncover, add the butter, if using, and lemon juice and tilt the dish to mix. Microwave, covered, on HIGH for 50 seconds more. Serve hot, warm or cool.

TOMATOES *AU NATUREL*

CALORIES PER SERVING: 60
SERVES: 4

At last, decent, juicy, red tomatoes, vine-ripened, sometimes grace our markets and greengrocers.

NOTE: For the same weight of smaller plum tomatoes, Flavourtop or Flavia, allow 3 or 4 minutes.

VARIATION
Add 8–12 shavings of Parmesan before the standing time. It melts and dribbles deliciously.

*4 large ripe plum tomatoes
(about 550g/1¼ lb)*
*8 fresh herb sprigs: basil, tarragon
or parsley*
*seasalt and freshly ground
black pepper*
1tbsp extra virgin olive oil
1 garlic clove, crushed

Set the tomatoes on their sides. Make 2 deepish diagonal cross-cuts on top. Set on a microwave-proof plate or in a ring dish. Microwave, uncovered, on HIGH for 5 minutes; halfway through, give the dish a quarter turn. Leave to stand for 2 minutes.

Push the herbs into the cuts on top and season. Spoon off the juices (about 3–4 tbsp) into a blender. Add the oil and garlic and whizz till pale pink and emulsified. Pour over the tomatoes.

AUBERGINES *AU NATUREL*
(WITH GARLIC-YOGURT DRESSING)

CALORIES PER SERVING: 60
SERVES: 4

It's fun to observe one of the remarkable bonuses of the microwave: aubergines cook so quickly and so perfectly that their flesh keeps its original green colour. An interesting way to serve an often neglected vegetable.

NOTE: For 1 × 275g/10oz aubergine, allow 6 minutes.

*2 aubergines (about 630g/1lb 6oz),
stalks intact*
8tbsp low-fat natural yogurt
2 garlic cloves, shredded
8g/¼ oz fresh mint leaves, snipped
*salt and freshly ground
black pepper*

Wipe the aubergines. Pierce each 5 or 6 times using a fork. Set on one sheet of kitchen paper, opposite each other (stalk to base). Microwave, uncovered, on HIGH for 10 minutes; halfway through, turn each one over and reposition (base to stalk). Cover and leave to stand for 2 minutes.

Holding the stalk end, slide a sharp knife, horizontally, down the length and through the stalk end to halve. Repeat with the other aubergine. Set the halves, cut sides down, on serving plates. Cross-slice each 12–15 times. Angle the slices. Dribble yogurt and garlic over each. Season and serve.

MANGETOUTS *AU NATUREL*
(WITH FROMAGE FRAIS & CHIVES)

CALORIES PER SERVING: 37
SERVES: 4

NOTES: For 50g/2oz, allow 1 minute. For 125g/4oz, allow 2 minutes.
Eat as a vegetable, or as a snack-cum-starter on garlicky bread, toast or crackers. Top, perhaps, with some cooked prawn, cured ham or smoked salmon shreds.

*225g/8oz mangetouts, washed,
not dried, and stalks snipped off*
4tbsp virtually-no-fat fromage frais
8g/¼ oz fresh chives, chopped
seasalt flakes (optional)

Toss the mangetouts, still wet, evenly over the bottom of the microwave (or on a microwave-proof plate if preferred). Cover loosely with microwave-safe clingfilm. Microwave on HIGH for 3¼ minutes. Leave to stand for 1 minute. Tip the mangetouts into a serving dish. Toss with the cheese, chives and salt, then serve.

CARROTS *AU NATUREL*
(WITH DILL & PUMPKINSEED OIL)

CARROTS MICROWAVE-COOKED WHOLE AND SLICED LATER WILL KEEP MORE OF
THEIR VITAMIN POWER AND NATURAL SWEETNESS. THE DARK PUMPKIN OIL (IF YOU CAN'T LOCATE
IT USE NUT OIL) AND SUMMERY HERBS GIVE A RATHER EXOTIC STIR-FRIED CRUNCHY EFFECT.

CALORIES PER SERVING: 50
SERVES: 4

NOTES: For 1 carrot, allow 2 minutes;
quarter the oil and herbs.
    For 2 carrots, allow 3 minutes;
halve the oil and herbs.

*4–5 large carrots
(about 450g/1lb)
1tsp kernöl (pumpkinseed oil)
8g/¼oz fresh dill sprigs*

Peel the carrots (or if young scrub
well), then prick each several
times. Set the whole carrots
around the edge of a large
microwave-proof plate or dish.
Cover with kitchen paper or a lid.

Microwave on HIGH for 4 minutes,
turning them over halfway through.
Leave to stand, covered, for
2 minutes.
    Discard the tip portion
(overcooked) and stalk end
(unappealing).
    Slice the remaining hot carrot
thinly and drizzle with the oil and
scissor-cut herbs. Serve hot, warm
or cold.

RED ONIONS *AU NATUREL*
(WITH CURRANTS)

ONIONS, FAMOUS FOR THEIR HEALTH-GIVING PROPERTIES, WHEN COOKED ALMOST WHOLE
LOOK LIKE BRILLIANTLY EXOTIC LOTUS FLOWERS. THEY TASTE REALLY SWEET AND SUCCULENT.
THE FRUIT AND HERB ACCOMPANIMENTS HELP TO ACCENTUATE THE EFFECT.

CALORIES PER SERVING: 62
SERVES: 4

NOTE: For 1 onion, allow
5 minutes.

*2 × 225g/8oz red onions,
skinned
2tbsp unsweetened apple juice
(preferably organic)
1tbsp currants
8g/¼oz fresh thyme leaves*

Pare the roots a little to help the
onions sit flat. Make two cross-
cuts almost to the base so the
onions will open out. Set on a
microwave-proof plate or ring
dish and spoon over the apple
juice and currants. Cover with a
lid, kitchen paper or microwave-
safe clingfilm.
    Microwave on HIGH for
6 minutes, then leave to stand for
2 minutes. Scatter over the thyme,
and spoon the juice and currants
over all. Serve half an onion per
person, hot or warm.

Potato Wedges *au Naturel*
(with soft cheese & spring onions)

Use flavourful, new-season, egg-size potatoes for this straightforward dish with its easy sauce. Estima, Charlotte, Belle de Fontenay and Roseval would all suit.

Calories per serving: 122
Serves: 4

Variation
Mash pan contents plus cheese and extra herbs along with 15g/½ oz butter.

550g/1¼ lb smallish, new-season potatoes, scrubbed
3tbsp stock or water
2 spring onions, chopped
3tbsp low-fat soft cheese, in small pieces
seasalt and freshly ground black pepper

Slice each potato lengthwise, then each half lengthwise to give quarters. Spoon the stock and half of the spring onions into the bottom of a large, microwave-proof casserole or steamer. Put the potatoes on top, cut sides down. Cover and microwave on HIGH for 8–9 minutes; halfway through, give the dish a half turn.

Leave to stand for 1 minute, then lift the potatoes into a serving dish.

Add the remaining spring onions and the cheese to the casserole and stir. Microwave, uncovered, on HIGH for 30 seconds. Stir, season to taste and pour the sauce over the potatoes. Serve hot or warm.

Baby Beetroot *au Naturel*
(with orange juice & fennel seeds)

Raw baby beetroot are no effort at all if cooked and prepared by this microwave method. The texture is dry, not waterlogged. Juice, oil and spices unlock their mellowness instead of vinegar knocking the taste for six.

Calories per serving: 48
Serves: 4

Note: For 175g/6oz, allow 6 minutes; halve the accompaniments.

Variation
Top rye bread with beetroot and their dressing, some salty blue cheese, crumbled, and a little parsley.

8–10 raw baby beetroot (about 350g/12oz), scrubbed
4tbsp freshly squeezed orange juice
1tbsp extra virgin olive oil
1tsp fennel seeds, roughly chopped

Reserve the beet greens, if present, for salad use, trimming off the stalks close. Pierce each beetroot 6 times. Scissor-trim long root tails to the bulb.

Place, wheel fashion, around the edge of a microwave-proof ring dish, casserole or plate. Add 2tbsp water. Cover with pierced microwave-safe clingfilm or a lid. Microwave on HIGH for 10 minutes, turning over the beetroot halfway through. Leave to stand, covered, for 2 minutes more.

Skin the still-hot beetroot by covering them with kitchen paper, pinching the skins and sliding them off.

Slice the hot beetroot, using a knife and fork, then drizzle with the juice, oil and fennel seeds. Stir and serve, still hot, on a bed of the reserved beet greens, if wished.

MUSHROOMS IN WINE *EN PAPILLOTE*

CALORIES PER SERVING: 78
SERVES: 4

Even without the lovage (an unusual herb: substitute celery tops if necessary), these mushrooms taste voluptuous and good. Serve as an accompaniment or on garlicky toasts as a snack.

225g/8oz mushrooms: oyster, button or flat field
25g/1oz butter, in tiny cubes
2tbsp dry sherry, dry vermouth or white wine
15g/½ oz fresh lovage (or celery tops), chopped
4tbsp virtually-no-fat fromage frais
seasalt and freshly ground black pepper

Remove and cross-slice long mushroom stalks. If using oyster or flat mushrooms, slice into 4 or 8 segments (depending on size). If using button mushrooms, quarter or halve.

Put the mushrooms, butter, wine of choice, most of the herbs, and the fromage frais into a medium microwave roasting bag. Seal loosely and set on a microwave-proof plate. Microwave on HIGH for 4 minutes; halfway through, carefully turn the bag over. Leave to stand for 2 minutes.

Knead the bag to blend the sauce-juice mixture evenly, and tip on to serving plates. Add the remaining herbs, season and serve.

PEPPERS *EN PAPILLOTE*

NOT ALL COOKED SWEET PEPPERS NEED SKINNING. THESE STAY TENDER, AND THE DRESSING, AS WELL AS HELPING PRESERVE VITAMINS, ADDS A VIVID BOOST. THE COLOURS ARE SENSATIONAL.

CALORIES PER SERVING: 30
SERVES: 4

VARIATION
Use to top hot pasta, a thin pizza or any hot flat bread, together with sliced low-fat mozzarella and a sprinkle of oregano.

350g/12oz peppers: red and yellow
4tbsp freshly squeezed orange juice
¼ tsp harissa (hot chilli paste)
seasalt flakes
8g/¼ oz coriander leaves, torn

Halve the peppers lengthwise. Discard stalks, pith and seeds. Slice each pepper half lengthwise into 6. Put the pepper sections in a microwave roasting bag. Seal loosely. Place on a microwave-proof plate.

Microwave on HIGH for 6 minutes; halfway through, carefully turn the bag over. Leave to stand for 2 minutes.

Carefully open the bag. Add the orange juice, harissa and salt to taste. Fasten the bag loosely and microwave on HIGH for 2 minutes more. Leave to stand for 1 minute.

Tip on to a serving dish. Scatter with torn coriander and serve.

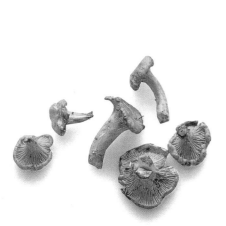

CELERIAC PURÉE *EN PAPILLOTE*

CALORIES PER SERVING: 130
SERVES: 4

Comfort food of great subtlety made tastier using microwave techniques. The added carrot gives colour and taste.

VARIATION
Substitute parsnip or swede for the celeriac.

550g/1¼ lb celeriac, peeled and cut into 1.5cm/½in cubes
1 medium carrot, scrubbed and cubed
150ml/¼ pint skimmed milk
¼ tsp grated nutmeg
freshly ground black pepper and seasalt flakes
25g/1oz butter
3tbsp low-fat yogurt
8g/¼ oz fresh parsley, chopped

Put the celeriac, carrot, milk, nutmeg and salt to taste in a large microwave roasting bag. Seal loosely and set on a microwave-proof plate. Microwave on HIGH for 12 minutes; halfway through, carefully rearrange the bag. Leave to stand for 2 minutes.

Tip the bag contents directly into a food processor. Add the butter and yogurt and process in brief bursts for a total of 20 seconds. Taste, season generously and transfer to a serving dish. Add the parsley and serve hot.

SWEET POTATO SHREDS *EN PAPILLOTE*

CALORIES PER SERVING: 158
SERVES: 4

Comfort food, but with a twist. It's just 10 minutes from go to whoa, using the coarse grater attachment of a food processor and a microwave bag. Serve as a curry or casserole accompaniment.

450g/1lb yellow- or orange-fleshed sweet potato, unpeeled and coarsely grated
3tbsp water
15g/½ oz butter
1tsp demerara sugar
15g/½ oz black poppyseeds
8g/¼ oz fresh mint, chopped

Put the grated sweet potato, water, butter and sugar in a microwave roasting bag. Seal loosely and set on a microwave-proof plate. Microwave on HIGH for 5 minutes; halfway through, carefully turn the bag over. Leave to stand for 2 minutes.

Add the poppyseeds and mint to the bag. Shake the bag contents lightly to mix. Empty out on to a serving dish.

BABY POTATOES *EN PAPILLOTE*
(WITH WINE & MINT)

CALORIES PER SERVING: 126
SERVES: 8

Succulent sweetness and the scent of mint makes these bag-baked, fat-free potatoes amazing. Little effort, great results! Leftovers (unlikely) taste excellent the next day.

1.5kg/3lb small, new-season potatoes
25g/1oz bunch of fresh mint
2 sugar lumps or 2tsp sugar
1tsp seasalt flakes
2tbsp white wine or stock
fresh mint to garnish (optional)

Scrub the potatoes. Prick each once with a fork. Pack into a large (turkey-size) microwave roasting bag or 2 medium bags. Add the remaining ingredients. Seal the bag(s) loosely. Set on a large, flat, microwave-proof dish. Microwave on HIGH for 10 minutes; halfway through, carefully turn the bag(s) over to reposition.

Empty the bag contents (mint, syrup and all) into a serving dish. Garnish with additional fresh mint if liked. Serve hot, warm or cool.

SPICED CABBAGE WITH SPRING ONIONS
EN PAPILLOTE

CABBAGE, TRADITIONALLY VALUED AS A LOW-CALORIE HEALING GREEN, IS NOW KNOWN
TO HELP COMBAT HEART DISEASE, CANCER AND EVEN RESPIRATORY DISEASES. TEMPT YOURSELF
WITH THIS EASY, SLIGHTLY ORIENTAL RECIPE WITH BITE AND STYLE. YOU'LL SAVE VITAMINS
AND KEEP A SWEET-SMELLING KITCHEN SINCE THIS COOKING METHOD DOES AWAY
WITH SULPHURY COOKING SMELLS.

CALORIES PER SERVING: 27
SERVES: 4

*350g/12oz cabbage: spring
greens, Savoy, white, green,
pak choy, choy sum, Chinese kale or
flowering cabbage*
6 spring onions, quartered
1 tbsp water
1 tsp light soy sauce or fish soy
½ tsp Chinese 5-spice powder

Quickly cross-shred the cabbage
into 5mm/¼ in strips. Put in a
medium microwave roasting bag
with the onions, water, soy and
spice. Seal loosely and set on a
microwave-proof plate.

Microwave on HIGH for
4 minutes (or less – say 3 minutes
only – for tender Oriental greens).
Carefully turn the bag over and
leave to stand for 2 minutes.
Shake, and serve hot.

RED CABBAGE, APPLE & JUNIPER
EN PAPILLOTE

ALTHOUGH TRADITIONAL WITH GAME, ROASTS AND TURKEY, THIS UPDATED,
ROBUST CLASSIC ALSO SUITS OILY FISH AND PORK. EAT IT AS A HOT SALAD, OR PILE IT
COLD ON TO BREAD WITH MUSTARD AND LEAN CURED BEEF FOR A DELI-STYLE
OPEN SANDWICH PAR EXCELLENCE.

CALORIES PER SERVING: 73
SERVES: 4

*225g/8oz red cabbage, thinly
shredded*
1 red onion, sliced
2 red-skinned apples, cored and sliced
4 tbsp raspberry vinegar
4–6 juniper berries, crushed
1 tbsp demerara sugar

Combine all ingredients in a microwave roasting bag. Seal loosely
and set the bag on a microwave-
proof plate. Microwave on HIGH
for 14 minutes; halfway through,
carefully turn the bag over using
tongs or oven gloves (it will be very
hot). Leave to stand for 2 minutes,
then tip and tilt the bag to mix the
contents. Serve hot, warm or cold.

RIGHT: SPICED CABBAGE WITH SPRING ONIONS *EN PAPILLOTE*;
RED CABBAGE, APPLE & JUNIPER *EN PAPILLOTE*

SPICED CAULI FLORETS *EN PAPILLOTE*

CALORIES PER SERVING: 69
SERVES: 4

Microwaved cauliflower, cooked with spices, takes on a whole new meaning after the sad, sulphury, waterlogged cauliflower of childhood memory. Eat with chicken or fish, or as a starter, perhaps, with poppadums, puris or naan bread.

3tbsp water
¼ tsp seasalt flakes
½ tsp tandoori spice blend
2.5cm/1in piece of fresh root ginger, grated or shredded
450g/1lb cauliflower, in small florets
4tbsp low-fat natural yogurt
2tbsp low-fat mayonnaise
15g/½ oz fresh herbs: coriander, parsley or chives
15g/½ oz seeds: sesame or black onion (nigella), or a mixture

Put the first four ingredients into a microwave roasting bag and knead. Add the florets and loosely seal.

Place on a microwave-proof plate and pat to flatten the contents. Cover with an upturned microwave-proof plate.

Microwave on HIGH for 8 minutes; halfway through, invert the bag and plate. Leave to stand for 2 minutes.

Open the bag and add the yogurt, mayonnaise and half the herbs, scissor-chopped. Pinch the bag closed, then knead, tip and tilt to mix the contents. Tip on to a serving dish and garnish with seeds and the remaining herbs.

GREEN BEANS WITH GARLIC *EN PAPILLOTE*

CALORIES PER SERVING: 63
SERVES: 4

Not all green beans microwave well but these taste delectable if young, tender beans are used, though there's no saving in time. The bonus is that they plump up nicely once the microwave turns itself off, and they never burn dry.

450g/1lb flat green runner beans, stringed and sliced diagonally into 1.5cm/½ in pieces
3tbsp water
1 small onion, shredded
2 garlic cloves, shredded
1tbsp walnut oil
½ tsp seasalt flakes
2tbsp chopped fresh parsley

Put the beans and water in a medium microwave roasting bag.

Seal very loosely and place on a microwave-proof plate. Microwave on HIGH for 8 minutes; halfway through, jiggle the bag to redistribute the beans outside to centre. Add the onion and garlic. Seal again and microwave on HIGH for a further 2 minutes. Leave to stand for 1 minute. Open the bag, add the walnut oil, salt and chopped parsley, toss and serve.

WILTED SALAD WITH TAMARILLO DRESSING

CALORIES PER SERVING: 80
SERVES: 4

Hot, but still crisp leaves dressed with a revolutionary, lively pink dressing. Instead of lemon or vinegar, tamarillo provides the acidity.

NOTE: Extra salad leaves, washed, drained and kept in a sealed plastic box or bag in the fridge, will remain crisp and delicious for several days (though you should expect some vitamin loss).

1 heart of oakleaf lettuce
2 heads of red or white chicory, halved
50g/2oz baby spinach leaves
1 head of radicchio
15g/½ oz herbs: rocket or parsley
1 tamarillo
2tbsp extra virgin olive oil

Wash the salad leaves and put, undrained, in a large microwave-proof salad bowl. Scatter over the herbs. Halve the tamarillo crosswise, scoop out and chop the flesh and put it in a blender. With the machine running, trickle in the oil until a deep pink emulsion results. Microwave the salad, uncovered, on MEDIUM (50%) for 3 minutes. Drizzle over some of the pink dressing and serve.

KIBBLED WHEAT WITH HERBS *EN PAPILLOTE*

CALORIES PER SERVING: 166
SERVES: 8

One of the original 'health foods', kibbled wheat still has an earthy charm. Cooked in a bag, it plumps up specially well. Mix with any garden or window box herbs or a supermarket 'fresh herb selection'. Excellent as an accompaniment for poultry, fish or game, this is also delicious served on rocket or baby spinach leaves as a starter.

225g/8oz kibbled wheat
1tbsp first pressing virgin olive oil
1 large onion, sliced
2 garlic cloves, chopped
50g/2oz toasted flaked almonds
2tbsp boiling water
1tsp seasalt flakes
15g/½ oz fresh herbs, chopped
15g/½ oz salted butter
freshly ground black pepper

Cover the kibbled wheat with hand-hot water and leave to soak for 30 minutes. Drain in a sieve.

Put the oil, onion and garlic in an open medium microwave roasting bag. Microwave on HIGH for 2 minutes or until aromatic. Leave to stand for 2 minutes, then carefully add the drained wheat, almonds, boiling water and salt. Seal the bag loosely and set it on a microwave-proof plate. Microwave on HIGH for 3 minutes; halfway through, turn the bag over. Leave to stand for 2 minutes.

Stir in herbs, butter and seasoning and serve.

PERFECT FROZEN PEAS *EN PAPILLOTE*

CALORIES PER SERVING: 100
SERVES: 2

A couch potato's delight: peas cooked in the very bag they came in. (If you have doubts about the material of the pack use a microwave roasting bag: some plastics are unsuitable for microwave cooking.)

NOTE: For 450g/1lb frozen peas (to serve 4), allow twice the herbs and butter and tip and tilt the bag halfway through.

1 × 225g/8oz bag frozen peas (any type)
2tbsp hot water
15g/½ oz mixed fresh herbs: parsley and mint, chopped
15g/½ oz salted butter, diced
salt and freshly ground black pepper

Make a 7.5cm/3in slit in the top centre of the pea bag and set on a microwave-proof plate. Spoon the water through the slit. Microwave on HIGH for 5 minutes. Leave to stand for 2 minutes. Spoon in the herbs, butter and seasoning. Tip and tilt the bag to mix the ingredients. Slit the bag and serve.

BRUSSELS SPROUTS *EN PAPILLOTE*

CALORIES PER SERVING: 75
SERVES: 4

A healthy, inexpensive but often unloved vegetable can be coaxed into deliciousness by using some Pacific-style ingredients.

350g/12oz small young Brussels sprouts, halved lengthwise
6tbsp stock or water
1 small fresh green chilli, seeded and crushed
4tbsp coconut cream powder
25g/1oz leek greens or spring onion tops, shredded
8g/¼ oz black onion seeds (nigella)

Put the sprouts, stock and chilli in a medium microwave roasting bag. Loosely seal and set on a plate. Microwave on HIGH for 4 minutes.

Carefully turn the bag over and leave to stand for 2 minutes.

Carefully open the bag and sprinkle in the coconut cream powder and half the leek shreds. Reseal and microwave on HIGH for 1 minute more. Leave to stand for 2 minutes.

Knead, tip and tilt the bag to mix the contents. Remove and discard the chilli.

Garnish with leek greens and black onion seeds.

SPICED POTATOES WITH RED LENTILS

CALORIES PER SERVING: 285
SERVES: 6

Here is a deliciously pretty Indian-influenced warm salad. Perfumed and stylish, it is great eaten with naan bread, with puris as a starter in its own right or else with fish and chicken.

2tbsp sunflower oil
125g/4oz split red lentils
350g/12oz leeks, finely sliced
4 garlic cloves, chopped
4tbsp coarse-chopped fresh coriander leaves
½ tsp seeds: cumin or fennel
½ tsp coriander seeds, crushed
½ tsp ground turmeric
10 green cardamoms, crushed, pods discarded
450g/1lb potatoes, in 1.5cm/½ in cubes
2 tomatoes, skinned and chopped
300ml/½ pint water
seasalt flakes and freshly ground black pepper
125g/4oz low-fat sheep's milk yogurt

Preheat a large browning dish in the microwave on HIGH for 6 minutes. Without removing the dish, add the oil and stir in the lentils, leeks, garlic, half the coriander leaves and all the spices. Stir, then cover and microwave on HIGH for 2 minutes.

Stir in the potatoes and tomatoes, then add the water. Cover and microwave on LOW (30%) for 25 minutes or until both lentils and potatoes are tender. Leave to stand for 1 minute.

Add seasoning to taste and garnish with the remaining coriander. Swirl the yogurt on top and serve the dish warm.

MAYAN MAIZE PURÉE WITH CHILLI

TO THE ANCIENT CENTRAL AMERICAN MAYAN PEOPLE, MAIZE (OR SWEETCORN, AS IT IS MORE COMMONLY KNOWN TODAY) SYMBOLIZED SUN AND RAIN. I CREATED THIS 'ETHNIC' RECIPE TO CELEBRATE THE FRESH TASTES OF SWEETCORN IN A NEW WAY.

CALORIES PER SERVING: 130
SERVES: 4

NOTE: Wash your hands well after working with hot chilli. Avoid rubbing eyes, nose or other sensitive skin.

2tbsp corn oil
1 large onion, chopped
150ml/¼ pint freshly squeezed orange juice
1tsp seeded, shredded fresh green chilli
3 whole fresh corncobs

Put the corn oil in a large microwave-proof jug or medium-sized dish with the chopped onion. Microwave, uncovered, on HIGH for 2 minutes or until translucent. Add the orange juice and chilli and microwave, uncovered, on HIGH for 2 minutes more.

Remove the leaves and discard the silk from the corncobs.

Coarsely grate off the kernels until only the naked cores remain. Discard these.

Spoon the sweetcorn paste into the jug. Microwave, uncovered, on MEDIUM (50%) for 6 minutes, stirring halfway through. The mixture should be hot, thickened and beginning to stick. Taste: when ready it is bright yellow, sweet and not starchy to taste.

Spoon into a serving dish lined, if wished, with some of the discarded green husks. Serve with main-course chicken, lamb or fish dishes, also as a filling for tortillas or as a toast topping.

RIGHT: SPICED POTATOES WITH RED LENTILS

HOT BROCCOLI
WITH ROQUEFORT DRESSING

BLUE CHEESE, SHERRY AND AVOCADO COMBINE WELL IN A PASTEL-GREEN SAUCE THAT
MAY REHABILITATE BROCCOLI EVEN FOR THOSE WHO LOATHE GREEN VEGETABLES. THE CUTTING
AND COOKING METHOD FOR BROCCOLI ENSURES PERFECT RESULTS.

CALORIES PER SERVING: 149
SERVES: 4

275g/10oz tender broccoli
4tbsp fino sherry
*25g/1oz blue cheese: Roquefort,
Lanark blue or Stilton, crumbled*
*2tbsp virtually-no-fat
fromage frais*
1 ripe avocado: preferably Hass
4tbsp chopped fresh parsley

Discard any very tough broccoli
bases, then thinly slice the
remaining stalks crosswise into
'coins' right up to the flowering
heads. Divide large heads in two
or three. Wash the broccoli but
don't shake dry.

Arrange the 'coins' and florets
in a microwave-proof ring dish
(florets with heads down). Cover
with a microwave-safe plate or
clingfilm. Microwave on HIGH for
4 minutes; halfway through, turn
the florets over using tongs.
Transfer the drained broccoli to
a microwave-proof serving dish.

Measure the sherry, cheese and
fromage frais into the still-hot ring
dish. Microwave, uncovered, on
HIGH for 1½ minutes, stirring
halfway through.

Scoop the avocado flesh
directly into a food processor or
blender. Add the parsley along
with the hot contents of the ring
dish. Whizz or blend until creamy.
(Alternatively, mash by hand until
semi-smooth.)

Pour the green dressing over
the broccoli. Microwave, covered,
on HIGH for 2 minutes to reheat.
Serve hot.

HOT CARROT SHREDS
WITH ORANGE & CORIANDER

CARROT LIKE YOU NEVER TASTED IT BEFORE: HOT, SWEET AND FRAGRANT WITH A BURST
OF CHILLI HOTNESS. THIS IS AS SIMPLE AS COOKING EVER GETS, YET THE FLAVOURS AND COLOURS
JUST SING OUT WITH FRESHNESS! GOOD EATEN AS A SNACK WITH CRUSTY BREAD
OR AS AN ACCOMPANIMENT.

CALORIES PER SERVING: 68
SERVES: 4

For speed, freshness and vitamin
retention, use the grating attachment
of a food processor to finely shred the
carrots. (Alternatively, use a
mandoline or hand-held grater.)

*550g/1¼ lb carrots, scrubbed and
finely shredded*
*1tsp Piri-Piri seasoning or dried
crushed chillies*
*½ tsp coriander seeds, crushed,
or ground coriander*
4tbsp freshly squeezed orange juice
*fresh flat-leaf parsley or dill
to garnish (optional)*

Put the carrots, spices and orange
juice in a shallow microwave-proof
serving dish or casserole. Cover
with a lid or plate. Microwave on
HIGH for 5 minutes. Stir, garnish
and serve.

HOT BROCCOLI WITH ROQUEFORT DRESSING; HOT CARROT SHREDS WITH ORANGE & CORIANDER

SAFFRON RISOTTO MAGNIFICO

CREAMY MASHED POTATO

CALORIES PER SERVING: 166
SERVES: 4

Microwave 'bake' large potatoes in their skins, then scoop out the interior for a particularly delicate mass (see Baked Potato 'Toppers', page 49). Otherwise cook new-season medium-sized potatoes as for Potato Wedges *au Naturel* (page 83) and mash them, skins and all.

GARNISHES
Try 15g/½ oz fresh parsley, chopped and/or ¼ tsp mild paprika. Or freshly grated cheese: Pecorino, Gruyère, Cheddar, Cabrales or Kephalotiri

550g/1¼ lb cooked potato flesh
4tbsp skimmed milk or low-fat natural yogurt
2tbsp extra virgin olive oil (optional)
½–1tsp seasalt flakes
½ tsp freshly ground black pepper
2 spring onions, chopped, or 2 garlic cloves, crushed

Combine all the ingredients in a large microwave-proof casserole or jug. Microwave, uncovered, on MEDIUM (50%) for 5 minutes or until the potato is evenly hot, and all liquid ingredients are heated. Mash using a potato masher or beat with a strong metal whisk. Or, if all else fails, mash with a large fork. The aim is to produce a light, not over-handled, creamy purée. Garnish and serve.

SAFFRON RISOTTO MAGNIFICO

CALORIES PER SERVING: 424
SERVES: 4

This risotto has a million-dollar taste though the actual ingredients cost surprisingly little. Don't, however, stint on the saffron. Microwaved risotto is self-timed, never sticks, never over-cooks and stays blissfully creamy.

600ml/1 pint hot vegetable stock
4tbsp extra virgin olive oil
225g/8oz short-grain white rice: Italian arborio or semi-fino (also called risotto rice)
1 leek, finely shredded
¼ tsp powdered saffron (or saffron threads, crushed)
150ml/¼ pint white wine: frascati or verdicchio
50g/2oz Parmesan cheese, in the piece
seasalt flakes and black pepper

To heat the stock: put it in a microwave-proof jug, cover and microwave on HIGH until boiling (about 5 minutes). Keep covered.

Put the oil into a large microwave-proof ring dish. Microwave, uncovered, on HIGH for 30 seconds or until hot. Stir in the rice, half the shredded leek and all the saffron. Microwave, uncovered, on HIGH for 2 minutes, stirring halfway through.

Gently stir in 150 ml/¼ pint of the hot stock. Microwave, uncovered, on HIGH for 2 minutes or until the liquid is absorbed. Repeat this process 3 times more: the rice will be swollen and moist. It will, however, still absorb almost all the liquid. Before the final addition of stock, during the 2 minutes the risotto is cooking, stand the wine, in a microwave-proof glass, in the microwave to heat as well.

Give the rice its final stir and add the hot wine and last portion of warm stock as well as the remaining leeks. Microwave, uncovered, on HIGH for the ritual 2 minutes.

Add half the Parmesan, shaved directly from the block, and stir. Add the salt and pepper. Microwave on HIGH for a final 2–3 minutes or until really tender and hot. Add the last shavings of Parmesan, cover and leave to stand for 45 seconds.

Serve the risotto with an accompanying undressed green salad and wash down with the remaining chilled wine.

WILD RICE & LEEK GREENS

EXPENSIVE, NUTTY-TASTING AND INTRIGUING, THESE BLACK GRAINS 'BUTTERFLY'
(HALF SPLIT OPEN) WHEN FULLY COOKED. WILD RICE CAN ACCOMPANY FISH, POULTRY AND VEAL DISHES
WITH STYLE AND WILL ALSO REHEAT WELL FOR A WARM SALAD, A DAY OR TWO LATER.

CALORIES PER SERVING: 137
SERVES: 4

125g/4oz wild rice
4 garlic cloves, chopped
½ – ¾ tsp seasalt flakes
600ml/1 pint boiling stock or water
1 young leek, sliced crosswise into very fine rings
1tbsp fruity olive oil
4tbsp chopped fresh herbs: chervil, chives, parsley or marjoram
1 small, crisp lettuce heart

Soak the rice in 600ml/1 pint hand-hot water for 3 hours. Drain in a sieve, discarding the water.

Put the rice, garlic, salt and finally the boiling stock or water into a deep, microwave-proof dish. Cover with a lid or microwave-safe clingfilm. Microwave on HIGH for 30 minutes or until the rice is tender and splitting.

Rinse the leek and drain. Stir into the drained rice with the oil. Cover and leave to stand for 1 minute.

Stir in herbs of your choice. Serve hot, warm or cold in a border of salad leaves.

RED RICE WITH VEGETABLES

CALORIES PER SERVING: 367
SERVES: 4

Rice cooked like this takes on a dense, rich texture. A good, peasanty dish for any occasion, substantial enough to eat on its own.

450g/1lb jar or can pimientos (red peppers)
225g/8oz short-grain white risotto rice
2 sprigs of fresh rosemary, crushed
1tsp each of dill and coriander seeds and dried crushed chillies
⅛ tsp saffron threads, crushed
4tbsp tomato purée
2tsp hot paprika
2tbsp extra virgin olive oil
6–8 small patty pan squash, halved or quartered
2 leeks, in 5mm/¼ in slices
125g/4oz cauliflower, in tiny florets
½ tsp seasalt flakes
12 black olives

Drain the pimientos, keeping the liquid. Add enough boiling water to the liquid to make up to 900ml/1½ pints. Combine the rice, pepper liquid, and rosemary in a large 28cm/11in diameter microwave-proof casserole. Cover and microwave on HIGH for 12 minutes.

Grind the dill and coriander seeds, chillies and saffron in an electric coffee grinder (or with a pestle and mortar). Stir these with the tomato purée, hot paprika and oil into the rice, along with the next 3 vegetables, leaving most of the leek greens on top. Microwave, uncovered, on HIGH for a further 12 minutes or until the rice is soft, the vegetables are cooked and the liquid mostly absorbed. Stir in salt.

Surround with the pimientos, cut into strips, and the olives. Microwave on HIGH for 1 minute longer. Cover and leave to stand (in the microwave) for a further minute, then serve.

WILD RICE & LEEK GREENS; MICROWAVE SQUARE 'CHIPS'; RED RICE WITH VEGETABLES

Plain Brown Rice & Variations

Microwaved rice is bliss – no sticking, lumping, boiling dry, bubbling over, no constant attention. Brown rice is white rice in its original bran coating. It is more nutritious, but also slower to cook, nuttier and denser. It takes a bit of getting used to and needs good seasoning. 'Parboiled', 'converted' or 'pre-fluffed' brown rice all refer to a steam treatment that drives useful vitamins back into the starchy interior and helps prevent the grains from sticking together, hence the other name, 'easy-cook rice'. Expect 'easy-cook' brown rice to cook in a slightly shorter time. For risotto see Saffron Risotto Magnifico (page 95).

CALORIES PER SERVING: 270
SERVES: 4

NOTE: For white rice, allow 225g/8oz rice, 450ml/¾pint boiling water and ½tsp seasalt. Microwave on medium (50%) for 9–12 minutes. Check as above and cook a little longer if needed.

VARIATIONS
1. Add 1tsp spicy Thai curry paste to the water. Add coconut cream instead of butter or oil. Omit extra salt.
2. Substitute 3tbsp low-fat mayonnaise for the butter or oil. Add the juice of 1 lime and stir in some cooked crab, prawns or shreds of smoked salmon.

225g/8oz brown rice
600ml/1 pint boiling water
½ tsp seasalt (optional)

ADDITIONS:
25g/1oz salted butter or
2 tbsp extra virgin olive oil
2 spring onions, leeks or
fresh chives, shredded
15g/½ oz fresh herbs: coriander,
flat-leaf parsley, mint or tarragon,
scissor-chopped
extra seasalt and freshly ground
black pepper

Put the rice in a large microwave-proof jug or casserole. Add the boiling water (and salt if wished) and cover with a plate or lid. Microwave on MEDIUM (50%) for 25 minutes. Check for doneness and absorption: if grains are still a little firm and water not all absorbed, microwave on MEDIUM (50%) for 10 minutes longer – 35 minutes in total.

Stir in the additions and serve the rice hot.

Mexican Turtle Beans with Coriander

CALORIES PER SERVING: 248
SERVES: 6

Black (turtle) beans need a good pre-soak and long cooking as well as assertive seasoning. But they taste excellent ('native caviar' is the ironic Latin American name) and never boil dry by this microwave method. Reheated and mashed they become frijoles refritos: perfect high-fibre partners for tortilla crisps, tacos or jacket potatoes.

VARIATIONS
1. If turtle beans are unavailable, substitute red kidney beans but test for doneness a little earlier: they may need less cooking time.
2. Add 100g/3½ oz fresh tomato, cubed.

350g/12oz dried black
(turtle) beans
4–5 fresh bay leaves, crushed
1 large onion, chopped
6 garlic cloves, chopped
2tbsp corn oil
1tsp ground cumin
3tbsp fruit vinegar: blackcurrant
or strawberry
1–2tsp seasalt flakes (to taste)
4tbsp scissor-cut coriander stalks
8–12 fresh coriander sprigs
to garnish

Rinse the beans and discard any debris. Drain. Put into a large, wide microwave-proof casserole and cover generously with boiling water. Microwave, uncovered, on HIGH for 12–14 minutes or until the water is boiling vigorously. Cover and leave to soak and soften for 2 hours, or if possible overnight.

At cooking time, drain off the water and add 900ml/1½ pints of boiling fresh water, the bay leaves, most of the onion and the garlic. Microwave, covered, on MEDIUM (60%) for 50 minutes or until the beans are tender and some skins split. Drain well.

Add the remaining onion, the oil, cumin, vinegar, salt and coriander stalks and stir.

Garnish the beans with the fresh coriander sprigs and serve hot or cold or with rice, chicken or turkey dishes.

MINT & BARLEY SALAD

CALORIES PER SERVING: 266 (FOR 4);
178 (FOR 6)
SERVES: 4–6

Pearl barley, usually banished to soups, is once again becoming noticed. Gelatinous and sweet, it is soothing, filling and rather intriguing. This peasanty dish is best served hot or warm and will reheat.

225g/8oz pearl barley
1tsp seasalt
¼ tsp ground mace
1tbsp extra virgin olive oil
2tbsp fruit vinegar: raspberry
6tbsp low-fat natural bio-yogurt
2tbsp low-fat mayonnaise
2 celery sticks, thinly sliced
25g/1oz fresh mint, chopped

Soak the barley in warm water in a deep microwave-proof bowl for 2 hours, then drain. Add 150ml/

½ pint boiling water, the seasalt and mace.

Cover and microwave on HIGH for 10 minutes. Leave to stand, covered, for a further 5 minutes.

Drain off any remaining water. Stir in the olive oil, vinegar, yogurt, mayonnaise, celery and some fresh mint.

Garnish the salad and serve hot with lamb, venison, beef or barbecued meats.

CHAYOTE RICE GUATEMALAN STYLE

CALORIES PER SERVING: 306
SERVES: 4

Chayote (also called choko or christophene) is a pear-shaped, pastel green vegetable not unlike marrow. Annatto (yellow vegetable colouring) from ethnic supermarkets is a brilliant storecupboard asset.

VARIATION
If no chayotes are available, use peeled cucumber or marrow, cut into chunks.

1 medium onion, chopped
2–3 garlic cloves, crushed
2 tbsp corn oil
225g/8oz easy-cook long-grain rice
½ tsp powdered annatto
600ml/1 pint boiling stock:
vegetable or chicken
2 chayotes, cubed
1tsp salt
25g/1oz coconut cream powder

In a deep casserole, toss the onion and garlic in the oil. Microwave, uncovered, on HIGH for 3 minutes. Add the rice, stir and cook on HIGH for 1½ minutes more. Stir in the annatto and stock. Cook on HIGH for 5 minutes. Add the chayote and cook on HIGH for 10 minutes. Stir in the salt and coconut. Cook on HIGH for a final 5 minutes.

MICROWAVE SQUARE 'CHIPS'

CALORIES PER SERVING: 158
SERVES: 4

Sizzle spice-dusted potato bits in a fraction of the oil normally associated with fried potatoes, for an interesting result. Though tasty, these 'chips' are hardly super-crisp, but they're mighty quick, easy and good for you and won't cause fat fires.

450g/1lb potatoes
1tbsp fécule (potato flour)
½ tsp Cajun seasoning or hot paprika
½ tsp tandoori seasoning or
garam masala
1tsp celery seeds, celery salt or
barbecue seasoning
2tbsp sunflower oil

Preheat a 25cm/10in diameter browning dish in the microwave, with one handle facing the front, for 8 minutes.

Cut the potatoes into 1.5cm/½ in

cubes and dry on kitchen paper. Put the potatoes into a plastic bag containing the *fécule*, seasonings and spices. Inflate the bag. Seal it, then shake it around well to coat the potatoes.

Partly remove the heated dish, add the oil and then empty in the potatoes, pushing them round the pan with a fish slice. Microwave, uncovered, on HIGH for 6 minutes, stirring halfway through. Garnish with extra salt. Serve hot or warm.

DESSERTS & PUDDINGS:
SWEET DIVERSIONS

I grew up eating wonderful desserts and delicious puddings and I still adore them. For this reason I have devised some lower-fat and less sweet (but often high-fibre) alternatives; versions which the microwave makes easy work of. Some people may be surprised to find hot, cold and frozen desserts in this book since the purest, classic 'true dessert' is still considered to be fruit and/or cheese. However, cheese all too often comes loaded with unhealthy saturates. Many microwaved fruit puddings have all the elegance of special-occasion restaurant desserts. They look sensational too and so they are great for entertaining.

Fresh fruits, cooked '*au naturel*', occupy many of these pages. Some cooked 'under wraps' (using leaves, paper or bags) also feature here. Follow cutting and preparation notes carefully, since skins split and fruits can cook unevenly unless pierced, cored or slashed, or evenly spaced to prevent steam build-up.

Low-fat soft cheese, low-fat yogurt and virtually-no-fat fromage frais tend to replace butter and cream in these recipes. They help to give a voluptuous 'mouth feel'. I prefer to achieve this effect naturally rather than by depending on the synthetic, texture-enhancing additives that are now prominent in so many factory-made foods.

Virtually-no-fat fromage frais with raw berries (a stylish continental habit) makes a brilliant dessert too. Another useful family dessert formula is a little of some home-made dairy pudding, custard or icecream, with added aromatics: cinnamon, citrus segments, cognac, rum, chocolate shreds or pure-fruit jam. It is best to add such flavours yourself rather than buy super-sweet, synthetically flavoured manufactured dairy desserts with their array of chemicals.

Since rice puddings, custards and fruit compotes all microwave superbly (and microwave-reheat perfectly as well), why not consider trying your hand at these traditional dishes? I've developed some lovely updates of old-fashioned comfort puddings as well, such as bread pudding, and others can be found in the breakfast chapter.

Cold and frozen puddings made ahead will last well for days in the fridge or freezer and can be eaten bit by bit. My single icecream recipe is a real party piece!

These recipes are far from austere. They celebrate fresh tastes, brilliant colour and real textures – and above all they explore the potential of microwave cooking for pleasurable results and good health.

LEFT: MANGO WITH LIME; QUICK CREAMY CUSTARD

PLUMS *AU NATUREL*

CALORIES PER SERVING: 144
SERVES: 4

Sticky plums that Tom Thumb would have been delighted by. Easy and unusual.

8 ripe, red, scented plums
(about 675g/1½ lb)
2tsp vanilla sugar
1 slice of gingerbread or
chocolate bread, crumbled
2tbsp fruit liqueur: crème de cassis
(blackcurrant), mûre (blackberry)
or other

Slash the plums down one side and remove the stones. Pack the plums, cuts uppermost, in a shallow, microwave-proof serving dish. Pierce each with a fork. Mix the sugar, crumbs and liqueur into a sticky mass. Spoon some of this into each plum.

Cover and microwave on HIGH for 5–6 minutes or until very hot and the juices are running. Serve hot or warm, with fromage frais.

APPLES *AU NATUREL*

REVISIT AN OLD FAVOURITE. NO CRISP SKIN BUT A BLISSFUL PURE, CLEAN APPLE FLAVOUR AND, FROM START TO FINISH, LESS THAN 20 MINUTES! IF WHIZZED UP IN A FOOD PROCESSOR, THEY MAKE A SUMPTUOUS, CREAMY DATE-APPLE OR FIG-APPLE PURÉE. PERFECT WITH GAME OR PORK, OR WITH BREAKFAST CEREAL AS A SNACK.

CALORIES PER SERVING: 98
SERVES: 4

NOTES: For 2 apples, allow 6–7 minutes; stand 2 minutes. For 1 apple, allow 3–4 minutes; stand 2 minutes.

4 flavourful apples: Cox's,
Jonathon's, Granny Smiths, Russets,
Golden Delicious (about 450g/1lb)
1tsp butter, in 4 tiny pieces
4 fresh dates, stoned and halved,
or 2 dried figs, chopped
½ tsp mixed spice
1 cinnamon stick, in long slivers
2tbsp water

Use a corer to core the apples. Thinly slit the skin around the outside of each apple and set on a large microwave-proof plate. Dot the apples with butter.

Add the dates or figs to the plate. Dust with the mixed spice and scatter the cinnamon slivers on top. Add the water.

Microwave, uncovered, on HIGH for 8 minutes; halfway through, give the plate a quarter turn and each apple a half turn (outside to inside). Leave to stand, covered, for 2 minutes.

Serve hot with the syrup that has formed spooned over. If puréeing, first remove the cinnamon slivers.

BERRIES *AU NATUREL*

CALORIES PER SERVING: 60
SERVES: 4

Hot, scented and shockingly sharp – that's how berries can taste when cooked sympathetically.

Eat plain, with little crisp biscuits, or spooned over icecream, rice, yogurt or muesli.

350g/12oz berries:
blackberries, boysenberries or
loganberries
¼ tsp ground allspice
2tbsp icing sugar

Put the berries into a round microwave-proof serving dish.

Pierce each berry right through with a fork. Dust with the allspice and most of the sugar.

Microwave, uncovered, on HIGH for 2 minutes. Leave to stand for 2 minutes. Stir, and serve dusted with the remaining sugar.

PEACHES *AU NATUREL*

CALORIES PER SERVING: 58
SERVES: 4

Summery peaches with a glorious difference. Eat them hot before the vivid colours fade, though the taste stays remarkable, even if eaten cold.

*2 large ripe peaches or
4 small ones
16 raspberries
2tsp jelly: raspberry or redcurrant
1 cinnamon stick, crushed
lengthwise
¼ tsp ground cinnamon
8 tiny dessert macaroons*

Cut the peaches in half, twisting to separate. Remove and discard the stones. Slice a sliver from the base of each half, so it sits evenly. Put 4 raspberries, ½tsp jelly, some long fragments of cinnamon stick and a pinch of ground cinnamon on top of each (or halve these quantities if using 8 peach halves).

Set the peaches around the edge of a microwave-proof plate or dish. Cover with a lid or loosely with microwave-safe clingfilm. Microwave on MEDIUM (50%) for 3 minutes; halfway through, give the plate a quarter turn, rotate each peach outside to inside, and cover again. Leave to stand for 2 minutes. Serve hot with 2 macaroons per serving.

RHUBARB *AU NATUREL*

CALORIES PER SERVING: 36
SERVES: 4

Rhubarb sweetened with apple, scented with cinnamon. Old-fashioned tastes achieved with minimum effort.

*450g/1lb rhubarb
2tbsp organic apple juice
concentrate
4tbsp hand-hot water
1 cinnamon stick, crushed*

Diagonally cut the rhubarb into 5cm/2in lengths. Put into a shallow microwave-proof casserole.

Drizzle with the apple concentrate, sprinkle over the water and tuck cinnamon stick fragments in between the pieces. Cover with a lid. Microwave on HIGH for 4–5 minutes or until the rhubarb feels tender when prodded but is not broken up. Serve over yogurt or fromage frais.

MELON WEDGES *AU NATUREL*

CALORIES PER SERVING: 53
SERVES: 4

Use citrus juice, scented leaves and heat to bring out melon's secret flavours. Easy and surprisingly delicious.

*1 ripe melon: Charentais or
Ogen, quartered
4tbsp freshly squeezed citrus juice:
blood orange, mandarin or clementine
8 fresh herb sprigs: spearmint or
bergamot
freshly ground black pepper
(optional)*

Scoop out and discard the melon seeds. Almost sever the flesh from the skin (leave it attached at both ends), then cut the flesh to give 8–10 triangular sections. Set the quarters around the edge of a large microwave-proof serving dish. Spoon some citrus juice over each. Loosely cover with greaseproof paper.

Microwave for 3–4 minutes or until warm and steaming. Scissor-chop half the herbs and scatter these over the fruit. Grind black pepper over all if liked.

Decorate with the remaining herb sprigs. Serve the melon wedges hot or warm.

MANGO WITH LIME

THE PLEASURE OF EATING HOT, SLIPPERY-SMOOTH, VOLUPTUOUS MANGO
FLESH IS CONSIDERABLE. DIRECT COOKING LIKE THIS MAXIMIZES TEXTURE,
EMPHASIZES FLAVOUR AND ALSO PROTECTS FOOD VALUES.

CALORIES PER SERVING: 125
SERVES: 4

VARIATIONS
1. Using the same method, substitute skinned, seeded pawpaw in slices or cubes, along with the pulp of 2 passionfruit.
2. Puréed with orange juice it makes a superb hot sauce.

1 large ripe mango or 2 medium ones (about 775g/1¾ lb)
grated zest and juice of 1 lime
banana leaf or baking parchment

Remove the skin of the mango then cut the flesh from the stone in long even slices. Alternatively, do not skin but cut the flesh in 2 large slabs from either side of the stone; cross-cut the flesh and slice it free from the skin as neat cubes. Add the lime zest and juice.

Wrap the fruit in some banana leaf or baking parchment, about 35cm/14in square. Fold, twist and secure with cocktail sticks.

Microwave on HIGH for 3 minutes. Unwrap at the table.

Serve alone, or with rice pudding, custard, natural yogurt or fromage frais.

SILKEN APPLE

AN ALMOST INSTANT BREAKFAST SNACK OR DESSERT. A FOOD PROCESSOR'S FINE
GRATING ATTACHMENT GIVES A PARTICULAR TEXTURE AND SWEET, VITAMIN-HIGH,
FRESH TASTE NOT POSSIBLE TO ACHIEVE BY HAND.

CALORIES PER SERVING: 125
SERVES: 2

Remove the stalks from 4 small, flavourful, crisp dessert apples. Fit the finest grating attachment to a food processor. Shred the apples, cores, pips and all. Divide in half.

Dust with cinnamon, cloves, nutmeg or allspice and add 1 tbsp of virtually-no-fat fromage frais to each serving. Eat quickly to enjoy the silky texture and fresh colour.

FIGS CARTOCCIO

CALORIES PER SERVING: 58
SERVES: 4

TO MAKE CARAMELIZED ALMONDS:
Add 2tbsp distilled malt vinegar and 50g/2oz caster sugar to a 25cm/10in microwave-proof dish and microwave, uncovered, on high for 5 minutes until the toffee is aromatic, evenly gold and bubbling. (Use gloved hands to tilt the dish if necessary, but do not stir.) Pour over 40g/1½ oz almonds on a heatproof surface. Leave to set and harden. Crush to a fine powder. Store and use as required.

40g/1½ oz caramelized almonds or purchased praline, crushed
2tsp anise liquor: anisette, ouzo or raki
4 ripe fresh figs
fresh fig leaves to decorate (optional)

Blend the crushed praline with the chosen liquor. Cut 4 greaseproof paper pieces, each 20cm/8in square. Make 2 cross-cuts down each fig, from the top nearly to the base. (They open like lotus flowers.) Place a fig on each paper square. Spoon some praline flavouring into the centre of each fig. Twist up the 4 corners of each paper square into parcels.

Microwave, evenly spaced, on HIGH for 1¾−2 minutes, depending on the size of the figs.

Unwrap the parcels at the table. Savour the aromas and contrast the sticky syrup with cold yogurt.

Figs Cartoccio

APPLE & BLACKBERRY *EN PAPILLOTE*

LITTLE PARCELS OF APPLES AND BERRIES WITH ALLSPICE MAKE EFFORTLESS INDIVIDUAL
DESSERTS. TRY THESE OCCASIONALLY WITH RICOTTA OR COTTAGE CHEESE,
WITH A FEW ALMONDS OR HAZELNUTS.

CALORIES PER SERVING: 104
SERVES: 4

*2 tart apples: Bramleys or
Granny Smith*

4tsp icing sugar

*½ tsp ground allspice or
mixed spice*

350g/12oz blackberries

Quarter and core the 2 apples.
Chop into small segments or cubes
and sprinkle with the sugar and
spice. Spoon into 10cm/4in piles
on 4 × 30cm/12in squares of
baking parchment. Top with the
berries (each pierced with a fork).
Twist up the paper points to make
neat parcels.

Microwave on HIGH for
3–4 minutes, depending on the
hardness of the apples. Serve hot
or warm, unwrapping at the table
and adding a dollop of ricotta.

PEAR & GINGER *EN PAPILLOTE*

PEARS, CUT LIKE MEDIEVAL CARVINGS INTO STRIPES, CAN BE BAKED
IN MINUTES INSTEAD OF HOURS. CURIOUS, DELICIOUS AND CALORIE-
EFFECTIVE AS WELL.

CALORIES PER SERVING: 120
SERVES: 4

4 ripe dessert pears

*2 portions stem ginger in syrup,
drained*

4tsp stem ginger syrup

*8 cardamom pods, crushed open
(optional)*

½ tsp icing sugar

Use a potato peeler or zester to
remove part of the skin from each
pear in 4 vertical bands. Use an
apple corer to remove the top
section of the cores, almost (but
not quite) cutting through to the
base. Slice a little of the base from
each fruit so it stands up evenly.
Set each pear on a triangle of
baking parchment (made by
cutting 2 × 35cm/14in squares
in half diagonally).

Chop the ginger into small
pieces and spoon one-quarter into
each pear. Trickle 1tsp of syrup
over each pear. Add 2 crushed
cardamom pods to each. Twist
the paper points closed and set the
pear parcels on a microwave-proof
serving platter.

Microwave on MEDIUM (50%)
for 16 minutes; halfway through,
give the dish a quarter turn and
the pears a half turn (outside to
insides). Microwave on HIGH for
a further 4 minutes, then leave to
stand for 2 minutes.

Partially unwrap and sift a little
of the icing sugar over each pear.
Unwrap completely at the table.

PRUNES IN COGNAC *EN PAPILLOTE*

PRUNES SEEM TO GET A BAD PRESS, WHICH IS A PITY SINCE THEY ARE SIMPLY
DRIED PLUMS – DELICIOUS, NUTRITIOUS, HIGH IN FIBRE, LOW IN FAT.
THEY ARE ALSO HELPFUL FOR THE DIGESTIVE SYSTEM.

**CALORIES PER SERVING: 175
SERVES: 4**

World-famous *pruneaux d'Agen*
would obviously taste sensational in
this recipe, but for everyday eating
Californian prunes are delectable too.
Combined with some apple, spices
and Cognac, they make an easy,
novel dessert with style.

*225g/8oz ready-to-eat
stoned prunes*
*1 red-skinned dessert apple,
quartered and cored*
4 pinches of ground cloves
4 pinches of caraway seeds
8tsp Cognac

Set a quarter share of the prunes
on each of 4 × 30cm/12in squares
of baking parchment. Thinly slice
the apple quarters into segments
and mix with the prunes. Add a
pinch of cloves and caraway seeds
to each portion.

Set on a microwave-proof
platter. Pull up all four corners
of each parcel and add 2tsp of
Cognac to each, then twist the
parcels closed.

Microwave on HIGH for
6 minutes; halfway through, give
the plate a half turn. Leave to
stand for 2 minutes.

Unwrap at the table and eat
while still warm and scented. Have
some virtually-no-fat fromage frais
available for those who like it, or
low-fat natural yogurt.

RED FRUIT COMPOTE

PLAIN 'STEWED FRUITS' HAVE THEIR USES. BUT PERFUMED SYRUPS, LIGHTLY THICKENED
AND GLOSSY, TURN SIMPLE FRUITS INTO SOMETHING MUCH MORE GRAND.
REFRIGERATED, THIS LASTS UP TO A WEEK.

**CALORIES PER SERVING: 112
SERVES: 8**

Great on breakfast cereal, low-fat
natural yogurt, sliced banana, or simply
on its own.

300ml/½ pint boiling water
50g/2oz caster sugar
300ml/½ pint orange juice
*1 vanilla pod, slit lengthwise
and flattened*
1 cinnamon stick, crushed
*350g/12oz scented red plums
or damsons*
*250g/9oz berries: brambles,
blackberries or loganberries*
*250g/9oz currants: white, pink,
red or black*
2tbsp arrowroot or fécule *(optional)*
4tbsp cold water (optional)

Combine the water, sugar, orange
juice, vanilla pod and cinnamon in
a deep, microwave-proof 2.5 litre/
4¼ pint ring dish. Microwave,
uncovered, on HIGH for 6 minutes.

Halve large plums; leave
damsons whole but prick them
with a fork. Add them to the syrup.
Microwave, uncovered, on HIGH
for 3 minutes or until tender.

Add the berries (each pricked
with a fork) and currants (pulled
from their stalks). Microwave,
uncovered, on HIGH for a further
3 minutes or until the juices have
run and the fruit is softened. Serve
hot, warm or chilled in glasses.

For an elegant thickened
compote, mix the arrowroot or
fécule with the water and stir into
the fruit juices. Microwave on
HIGH for 3 minutes until thickened.
Stir the compote to mix fruits and
syrup evenly. Serve hot or cold.

BERRY PARFAIT ICECREAM

THIS CHEERFUL, PINK PARTY-STYLE ICECREAM NEVER FAILS. TOASTED BREADCRUMBS
AND RAW SUMMER FRUITS COMBINE IN AN UNEXPECTEDLY STYLISH WAY. CELEBRATE SUMMER
EVEN ON GREY DAYS WITHOUT CRASHING YOUR CALORIE LEVELS.

CALORIES PER SERVING: 188
SERVES: 5
(MAKES 1 LITRE/1¾ PINTS)

RAW BERRY COULIS

*This scented, glossy sauce is the
perfect topping for Berry Parfait
Icecream. Put 175g/6oz fresh or
thawed raspberries, mulberries,
loganberries or blackberries with
2tbsp eau de vie (use framboise,
fraise or Poire William) and
6tbsp sweet white wine (use Pineau
des Charentes or Muscat) into a
blender. Liquidize well, then rub
through a plastic sieve. Chill.*

*½ tsp almond or
other tasteless oil
50g/2oz granary bread, cubed
and crumbed
2 egg whites (size 3)
pinch of salt
40g/1½oz vanilla sugar
225g/8oz redcurrants or
other red berries
125g/4oz blueberries
175g/6oz virtually-no-fat
fromage frais
2tbsp fruit liqueur: framboise
(raspberry) or fraise (strawberry)
eau de vie (optional)
1 × 11g/0.4oz sachet or
1tbsp powdered gelatine
3tbsp cold water*
SYRUP:
*50g/2oz caster sugar
7tbsp boiling water*

Foil-line the bottom and long sides
of a 1 litre/1¾ pint terrine or
900g/2lb loaf tin, allowing a little
extra to overhang. Brush lightly
with the almond oil.

Preheat a browning dish in
the microwave for 5 minutes
(or according to manufacturer's
instructions). Put the fresh
breadcrumbs in the dish and
microwave, uncovered, on HIGH
for 3 minutes or until toasted.
Leave to cool.

Put the egg whites and salt in
a deep bowl and whisk, using an
electric beater, till soft peaks form.
Continue whisking, gradually
sprinkling in the vanilla sugar,
until the peaks will stand up firmly.

Add the prepared fruit and
any juice to the crumbs and mash
together to an even red. Fold the
fromage frais into the fruit-crumb
mixture, adding the liqueur.

Sprinkle the gelatine over the
cold water in a microwave-proof
cup or jug. Leave to swell for
5 minutes. Microwave, uncovered,
on HIGH for 1 minute or until
dissolved. Leave to cool.

For the syrup, measure the
sugar and boiling water into a
small microwave-proof dish. Swirl
to dissolve the sugar. Microwave,
uncovered and undisturbed, on
HIGH for 3–4 minutes or until a
clear bubbling syrup forms
(109°C/225°F on a sugar
thermometer, if tested). Pour this
syrup immediately on to the egg
whites, whisking steadily, followed
by the gelatine mixture.

Fold the egg white mixture into
the fruit and crumb mixture.
Quickly smooth into the terrine
or tin. Cover and fast-freeze for
5–6 hours or until firm, then reduce
to normal freezer temperature.

To unmould: slide a knife blade
around the edges. Pull up the foil
at both sides to lift and loosen the
contents. Invert on to
a chilled dish. Remove the foil.
Leave at room temperature for
10–15 minutes. Alternatively,
soften in the microwave on MEDIUM
(50%) for 10–15 seconds; leave to
stand for 2–3 minutes.

RIGHT: BERRY PARFAIT ICECREAM WITH BERRIES *AU NATUREL*

BREAD PUDDING

HOMELY AND DELICIOUS, THIS IS OLD-FASHIONED COMFORT FOOD AT ITS BEST.
THIS VERSION WITH RUM AND DATES IS MY OWN INVENTION, AS THE MICROWAVE
METHOD WORKS QUICKLY AND WELL.

CALORIES PER SERVING: 233
SERVES: 6

12 slices of French baguette
4 fresh dates, stoned and sliced
2 eggs and 1 egg yolk (size 3)
1tbsp soft dark brown sugar
300ml/½ pint skimmed milk
150ml/¼ pint whole milk
2tbsp liquor: dark rum, whisky or brandy (optional)
½ tsp vanilla essence
pinch of salt
2tbsp reduced-sugar apricot jam
1tbsp freshly squeezed juice: blood orange or mixed raspberry and orange

Overlap the bread slices in 2 lines down the length of a microwave-proof oval pie dish or casserole (about 1.75 litre/3 pint volume). Scatter with dates. Whisk, blend or food process together the eggs, sugar, milks, liquor, vanilla and salt. Pour this mixture over the bread. Stand for 10 minutes (no longer or it soaks up too much).

Microwave, uncovered, on HIGH for 4 minutes. Give the dish a half turn and microwave for 2–3 minutes more. (No runny custard mixture should be visible at the base of the bread.) Remove the pudding, cover and set aside while the glaze is made.

Put the jam and juice in a microwave-proof jug or dish. Microwave, uncovered, on HIGH for 1¼ minutes. Stir well and paint over the surface of the pudding. Replace the dish and cook for a further minute on HIGH. Serve hot or warm.

QUICK CREAMY CUSTARD

MY MOTHER CALLED HER (PRE-MICROWAVE) VERSION OF THIS, ICECREAM CUSTARD.
MY CUSTARD HAS THE SAME OLD-FASHIONED CHARM YET IS RIDICULOUSLY SIMPLE AND NEVER
STICKS ON THE BOTTOM. EAT PLAIN, WARM OR COOL, WITH SLICED FRESH FRUIT,
OR FROMAGE FRAIS, NUTS AND A DUSTING OF COCOA.

CALORIES PER SERVING: 82
WITH BUTTER: 108
SERVES: 4

3tbsp flour or custard powder
1tbsp dark soft brown sugar
450ml/¾ pint skimmed milk
15g/½ oz butter (optional)
1 egg (size 3)
4tbsp virtually-no-fat fromage frais
1tbsp liquor: dark rum or brandy

In a large microwave-proof jug or medium bowl, stir the flour and sugar together. Whisk in the milk and add the butter, if using. Microwave, uncovered, on HIGH for 6 minutes, whisking briefly after 4 and 5 minutes.

Add the egg. Whisk again and microwave on HIGH , uncovered, for 1 minute more. Whisk in the fromage frais and then the liquor. Serve warm or cool.

GIN-LIME JELLY WITH GRAPES

BECAUSE FRESH JUICE, ZEST AND GOOD WHITE WINE ARE USED IN THIS JELLY IT HAS A TASTE
ALL OF ITS OWN. THE LIQUOR IS A FINAL FLOURISH. IF THE WEATHER IS COLD AND YOU CAN PREPARE
IT 24 HOURS AHEAD, USE 1 SACHET LESS OF GELATINE, FOR A MORE TENDER SET.

CALORIES PER SERVING: 134
SERVES: 6
(MAKES 900ML/1½ PINTS)

5 tbsp cold water
3 × 11g/0.4oz sachets or 3 tbsp
powdered gelatine
125g/4oz caster sugar
250ml/9fl oz boiling water
250ml/9fl oz medium dry
white wine: Riesling
finely grated zest and juice of 2 limes
5–8 drops (not shakes) edible green
colouring (optional)
4tbsp gin (optional)
125g/4oz green seedless grapes, halved
extra green grapes and leaves to
decorate (optional)

Measure the cold water into a microwave-proof bowl. Sprinkle the gelatine over and leave to swell for 5 minutes. Have ready a 900ml/1½ pint jelly mould of choice.

Stir the sugar and boiling water into the gelatine to dissolve it. Microwave, uncovered, on HIGH for 30 seconds. Add the wine, lime juice and colouring. Cool over iced water. Stir in the gin if using.

Pour about one-third of the liquid jelly into the mould. Stand the mould in iced water in the fridge for about 20–30 minutes or until set. Add the lime zest and grapes to the remaining jelly mixture.

Stand this in the fridge, also over iced water, until near setting point, then spoon this over the base layer. Chill for 6–8 hours or until firm (or, preferably, overnight).

To unmould: loosen the jelly by drawing it back from the sides of the mould with the fingers. Run a sharp knife point round the edge. Dip up to the rim in hand-hot water for about 10 seconds (no longer), then briskly invert on to its plate, giving a sharp shake. (Repeat the process if unsuccessful.)

Decorate, if liked, with little bunches of grapes and leaves.

FROZEN KIWI INSTANT SORBET

CALORIES PER SERVING: 70
SERVES: 4

Kiwi fruit are also exceedingly good in a fruit salad for breakfast or brunch. Halve 2 kiwi fruit, 2 passionfruit, 2 tamarillos. Put one of each fruit half on a plate and eat with a teaspoon as for a boiled egg. Delicious and only 49 calories per serving.

6 kiwi fruit
3tbsp caster sugar
grated zest and juice of
1 lime
4tbsp virtually-no-fat
fromage frais
edible flowers or herb leaves
tuile biscuits (optional)

Halve the kiwi fruit and scoop out the flesh. Place it on a baking tray lined with greaseproof paper and

freeze overnight. At serving time, put the frozen fruit, sugar, lime zest and juice into a food processor. Process for a little over a minute to an icy, semi-smooth mass. Scoop quickly into 4 pretty stemmed glasses.

Add a dollop of fromage frais to each. Decorate with edible flowers or herb leaves and, if liked, tuiles or spicy wafer biscuits.

DRINKS, SAUCES & DIPS:
LIQUID ASSETS

The details that are most cherished and remembered from meals we have taken at restaurants, cafés and friends' houses are frequently the little extra food items and the drinks we hadn't expected. This chapter contains many well-loved recipes (some cooked, some raw and many rather eccentric) which, if used imaginatively, can add excitement to your meals. Many of them have been prompted by food and drinks that I have tasted on my travels, adapted into dishes that are relevant for keeping a low-fat, high-health diet interesting and lively.

All too often we reach for commercially prepared, synthetically flavoured and sweetened soft drinks, simply because we haven't been aware of the alternatives. Now, the microwave makes creating a new drink easy. Lemon barley water, for example, a tonic and thirst-quencher, gains new relevance.

Many of these drinks could become long iced drinks, a hot toddy (add boiling water and then microwave) or a cocktail base (add extra liquor and some ice cubes). Most are based on fruits, fruit pastes, dried flowers, herbs and chocolate, spices and rum. Use of the microwave means that their full scent is preserved. True tastes and colours rather than faded overcooked effects make a huge difference.

Relishes and pickles can revitalize sandwiches, pasta or rice. Pungent home-made pesto, in soups, on potatoes or with crudités, is a nod to Italy but the difference between bought and fresh is a revelation.

Chilli-style sauces and even béchamel, microwaved, are hugely versatile because they can act as dips, spreads, pour-over accompaniments to cold and hot vegetables, for poppadums, noodles or kebabs, and as the items that pull foods together into one unified dish. A creamy béchamel with crab, herbs and lemon can be a filling for hollowed-out baby tomato halves or, with extra fromage frais, a dip for celery or chicory leaves.

Many traditional sauces involve endless stirring over a hot stove and the risk of lumping and scorching on the bottom of the pan. The microwave makes these points obsolete. Microwave-cooked béchamel tastes so good that even a sweet version is possible.

Use a seasoning mixture to prevent boredom. My dry nut and multi-spiced recipe (page 125) is based on an African seasoning, *tsire*. Condiments like these can help to keep your mind off the addition of other higher-fat flavourings, used out of habit.

To consider food as just fuel is missing the point. Treat food and drink with wit and learn to improvise – eating and drinking are rituals too precious not to be celebrated every day of our lives.

LEFT: INSTANT HOT ORANGE *PRESSÉ*; LEMON BARLEY WATER

INSTANT HOT ORANGE *PRESSÉ*

IT'S EASY TO FORGET THAT WITH WHOLE JUICY CITRUS FRUITS, FLAVOURINGS
AND WATER, YOU CAN MAKE YOUR OWN VITAMIN-HIGH, FLAVOURFUL LOW-CALORIE DRINK.
GINGER ADDS ITS NATURAL TONIC EFFECT TOO.

CALORIES PER SERVING: 35
SERVES: 1

*1 small orange (or lemon
or lime)*
1 sugar lump
½ cinnamon stick, crushed
*1.5cm/½ in fresh root ginger,
crushed (optional)*
150ml/¼ pint boiling water

Slice half the orange into a large microwave-proof glass. Add the juice squeezed from the second half, the sugar, cinnamon and ginger. Crush with a teaspoon or fork. Top up with the water. Stir.

Microwave, covered, on HIGH for 1½ minutes. Leave to stand for 30 seconds, then uncover, stir, savour and sip. This drink is a sloth's delight with a fraction of the calories of commercially prepared orange juice or drink.

LEMON BARLEY WATER

ALL BARLEY, BUT PARTICULARLY POT BARLEY, CONTAINS GOOD AMOUNTS OF CALCIUM,
POTASSIUM AND B VITAMINS. IT ALSO CONTAINS BETA GLUCANS – KNOWN TO BE CHOLESTEROL-
LOWERING. IT SOOTHES THE URINARY AND DIGESTIVE TRACTS TOO.
NO WONDER IT'S BEEN SO LOVED FOR CENTURIES.

CALORIES PER SERVING: 53
(4TBSP EACH)
SERVES: 12
(MAKES 750ML/1¼ PINTS)

This pale, cloudy drink is surprisingly easy and inexpensive to make. Keep refrigerated and encourage young people to learn this recipe – it beats most purchased soft drinks! Pot barley is less easy to find than pearl barley – try health food shops, otherwise use pearl barley.

VARIATION
Substitute 1 mineola or small orange for 1 of the lemons.

125g/4oz pot barley
1 litre/1¾ pints boiling water
grated zest and juice of 3 lemons
50g/2oz caster sugar

Put the barley into a clean coffee grinder and grind in several 3-second bursts, until coarse-chopped (over-grind and you'll end up with flour). Put the chopped barley in a large microwave-proof jug, at least 2 litre/3½ pint capacity. Add the boiling water and stir. Microwave, covered, on LOW (30%) for 12 minutes or until the liquid has slightly thickened. Stir, cover again and microwave on HIGH for 1½ minutes or until just under boiling point (longer and it may boil over).

While the barley cooks, mix the lemon zest and juice with the sugar in a heatproof jug or bowl.

Strain the hot barley liquid through a non-metal sieve into the juice and sugar mixture. Leave to stand for 2 minutes, then strain the liquid back through the barley, into the original jug. (If there is less than 750ml/1¼ pints, pour a little extra boiling water through the barley to make it up to volume.) Pour into a sterilized bottle. Cool and refrigerate.

To use, dilute using 2 parts of cordial (4tbsp for each serving) to 3 parts iced water (6tbsp).

PEPPERMINT & LEMON HONEY 'TEA'

CALORIES PER SERVING (WITHOUT VODKA): LARGE 11; SMALL 5
MAKES: 4 LARGE OR 8 SMALL GLASSES

2 peppermint teabags
600ml/1 pint boiling water
4tsp flower-scented honey
1 lemon, sliced into 8
4 fresh mint sprigs
4tbsp vodka or dry gin (optional)
extra herbs to decorate (optional)

Make the tea with the boiling water in the usual way. Cover and allow to stand for 3 minutes. Strain into glasses, pressing the teabags well. Stir in the honey and add the lemon slices and mint. Drink while hot, as a restorative. Alternatively, chill and serve over ice as an aperitif to stimulate the appetite at night, with a dash of liquor.

JUICE SPECIAL

CALORIES PER SERVING (150ML/¼ PINT EACH): 124
SERVES: 4 (MAKES 600ML/1 PINT)

A juicer is essential. Invest in one: it will revolutionize your attitude to fruit drinks.

Into a juicer put, in mixed batches: 2 large Cox's apples, quartered and cored; 3 under-ripe bananas, in chunks; 2 oranges, quartered, peeled, then cubed; and 8 ice cubes. Process. Add a splash of mineral water. Serve fresh and frothy with a mint sprig. Drink a double serving for breakfast or an afternoon pick-me-up.

SCARLET STRAWBERRY CORDIAL

CALORIES PER SERVING (1TBSP EACH): 17
SERVES: 40 (MAKES 600ML/1 PINT)

Make this sensational vivid pink cordial whenever decent strawberries are available. It has a versatility which means it is perfect in long sparkling iced party drinks, over icecream as a syrup, as part of an icecream soda (for children), spooned over fromage frais, or with sliced fresh fruits such as peaches, nectarines, melon, mango and pawpaw. The alcohol helps to preserve, fortify and flavour the drink.

225g/8oz fresh scented strawberries, hulled
85g/3oz caster sugar
150ml/¼ pint boiling water
½ tsp tartaric acid
150ml/¼ pint iced water
6 ice cubes, crushed
4tbsp fruit brandy or eau de vie: fraise (strawberry) or other
4tbsp dry gin

Quarter the wiped but unwashed strawberries. Put them in a blender or food processor.

Put the sugar and boiling water in a large microwave-proof jug with the tartaric acid. Microwave, uncovered, on HIGH for 1½ minutes, stirring halfway through.

Pour the boiling hot syrup over the strawberries and quickly blend or process until scarlet, foamy and smooth. Add the iced water, the ice cubes and the liquors. Blend or process again. Strain through a non-metal sieve to remove the seeds.

Pour into a hot sterilized bottle or jar. Seal, preferably using a plastic, acid-proof screwtop lid. Allow to cool, then store in the coldest part of the refrigerator for up to 2 weeks.

Serve in a chilled jug, allowing 1tbsp cordial per person with extra ice (no more than 6 cubes) and the mixer of your choice (dry champagne, sparkling white wine or soda water). In summer, add some fresh strawberry leaves and blossoms if available.

CHOCOLATE DRINK

MAKE SOME OF THIS INTENSE CHOCOLATE MIXTURE NOW AND THEN AND KEEP
IT ON HAND IN THE REFRIGERATOR. IF YOU ARE FEELING VIRTUOUS JUST USE 1TBSP,
DILUTED WITH BOILING WATER FOR A MILD CHOCOLATEY DRINK. FOR A MORE INTENSE
FLAVOUR, YOU NEED 2TBSP. ADD MILK TO TASTE.

CALORIES PER SERVING (2TBSP EACH): 87
SERVES: 15

USES
1. Add iced skimmed milk instead of water for a splendid chocolate shake. Shake or whisk well.
2. For a hot drink, add boiling skimmed milk instead of water and stir well.
3. For a cocktail, shake with skimmed milk and add 2tbsp extra rum per serving and ice.

2tbsp olive oil
200g/7oz golden syrup
85g/3oz cocoa (not drinking chocolate)
1tsp ground cinnamon
2tsp vanilla essence
8tbsp cold water
6tbsp liquor: brandy or dark rum
150ml/¼ pint boiling water

Combine the first 5 ingredients in order in a large, microwave-proof jug or bowl. (To measure accurately, set the syrup and the cocoa on the scales and remove the required amounts directly into the jug.) Stir until the smooth.

Microwave, uncovered, on MEDIUM (50%) for 4 minutes, then on HIGH for 4 minutes or until really chocolatey-scented and densely bubbling (a sugar thermometer should just hover between 85°C/185°F and 94°C/200°F, but should not exceed that temperature). Whisk in the cold water. Cool, then add liquor. Whisk in 150ml/¼ pint boiling water, cool and refrigerate the concentrate. Add water or milk as preferred for a long drink.

AMARDINE APRICOT VELVET DRINK

THIS HEAVENLY DRINK IS TRADITIONAL EGYPTIAN FARE. COMPRESSED PASTE OF APRICOT
(AMARDINE), IN SHEETS, CAN BE FOUND IN MOST GREEK AND ORIENTAL GROCERS. STORE SOME
ON YOUR LARDER SHELVES. (INCH-SQUARE, JEWEL-BRIGHT PIECES MAKE FRUITY SNACKS TOO,
WITH NUTS AND SEEDS.) SERVE THE DRINK COLD, DILUTED OVER ICE, OR HOT AS A TEA. IT KEEPS
WELL IN THE REFRIGERATOR FOR SOME WEEKS.

CALORIES PER SERVING (75ML/2½ FL OZ EACH): 100
SERVES: 16 (MAKES ABOUT 1.1 LITRES /2 PINTS)

VARIATIONS
1. For hot tea, half-fill a microwave-proof glass or mug with drink mixed 50:50 with water. Microwave, covered, on high for 1½ – 2 minutes per large mug. Leave to stand for 1 minute.
2. Trickle one diluted tablespoon of the drink over sliced, fresh apricots, melon, bananas or lichee halves for an exotic dessert, with mint as a garnish.

450g/1lb amardine sheets (or sulphured dried apricots)
1 litre/1¾ pints boiling water
50g/2oz granulated sugar
grated zest and juice of 1 lemon or orange
2tsp rosewater or orange flower water, or a mixture
fresh mint sprigs to garnish (optional)

Put the cut-up amardine (or washed, scissor-chopped apricots) into a 4 litre/7 pint microwave-proof casserole or jug. Add the boiling water and stir. Microwave, covered, on HIGH for 5 minutes. Stir well, then microwave, covered, on HIGH for a further 3 minutes. Leave to stand for 5 minutes.

Add the sugar, zest and juice, and flavouring. Measure the volume and add cold water to make up to 1.1 litres/2 pints.

Pour into a blender. Blend until perfectly smooth. Chill, then pour into a sterilized bottle.

Dilute half and half with spring water over ice cubes, adding a mint sprig to each glass if liked.

TRINIDADIAN ROSELLA DRINK

CALORIES PER SERVING (4TBSP EACH): 25
SERVES: 15 (MAKES 900 ML/1½ PINTS)

This dried bloom, rosella (roselle, Jamaican sorrel, often confusingly called hibiscus in health food stores) is a main ingredient in many herbal teas.

VARIATION
Stir into boiling water with an additional sugar cube and 1 extra tbsp of dark rum for a glorious winter toddy.

50g/2oz dried rosella (hibiscus) flowers
2 cinnamon sticks, crushed
8 cloves
zest (in several pieces) and juice of 1 lime
1 litre/1¾ pints boiling water
50g/2oz caster sugar
6tbsp dark rum

Put all the ingredients, except the sugar and rum, in a microwave-proof jug. Stir and microwave, covered, on HIGH for 10 minutes. Stir again. Leave to stand, covered, for 5 minutes.

Strain and return to the jug. Add the sugar, stir, cover and microwave on HIGH for 3 minutes. Cool and add the rum. For each serving, stir 4tbsp into 150ml/¼ pint ice-cold water.

TAMARILLO RELISH

CALORIES PER SERVING (2TBSP EACH): 32
SERVES: 20

VARIATION
Purée two parts relish with one part fruit juice or dry white wine in a blender for a scarlet coulis. Great for grills and barbecues.

NOTE: To sterilize jars or bottles, place clean, washed glass jars, upside down (bottles on their side), on a sheet of kitchen paper on a microwave rack. Microwave, uncovered, on high for 2–3 minutes. Remove with oven-gloved hands, as they will be extremely hot.

3 large red tamarillos (about 350g/12oz)
1 large dessert apple, cored and chopped (about 175g/6oz)
85g/3oz caster sugar
1 medium red onion, chopped
2.5cm/1in piece of fresh root ginger, shredded
¼ tsp chilli seasoning or chilli powder
6tbsp distilled white malt vinegar

Halve the tamarillos lengthwise. Place them, cut sides down, in a flat-bottomed microwave-proof casserole. Microwave, uncovered, on HIGH for 4 minutes. Using tongs, remove the hot skins and stalks and discard. Scissor-chop the hot fruit. Add the remaining ingredients. Cover and microwave on HIGH for 16 minutes, uncovering halfway through and stirring from sides to centre. Leave uncovered for the remaining cooking time.

Pour into hot, sterilized jars, label and seal.

AMERICAN PICKLES

CALORIES PER TABLESPOON: 24
MAKES: 775G/1¾ LB

VARIATION
Substitute black onion seeds (nigella) for the black mustard seeds if liked.

1 large cucumber (about 450g/1lb), thinly sliced
2–3 onions (about 350g/12oz), sliced
2tbsp table salt
225ml/8fl oz malt vinegar
100g/3½ oz granulated sugar
2tsp yellow mustard seeds
1tsp black mustard seeds (optional)
1tsp celery seed
½ tsp ground turmeric

Sprinkle the sliced vegetables with salt. Stir and leave to stand for at least 30 minutes. Drain in a sieve, pressing well to extract all liquid.

Combine the remaining ingredients in a large microwave-proof casserole. Microwave, uncovered, on HIGH for 5 minutes or until hot and steaming.

Add the vegetables and stir. Cover and microwave on HIGH for a further 8 minutes or until bubbling violently and very syrupy.

Pour into sterilized jars, label and seal with non-metal lids.

CLASSIC VINAIGRETTE

CALORIES PER TABLESPOON: 95
MAKES: 225ML/8FLOZ

Wonderful, but make a little go far –
a calorie bonanza!

Put 175ml/6fl oz extra virgin olive
oil, 3tbsp white wine vinegar,
1tbsp Dijon mustard and ½ tsp
each of seasalt flakes and crushed
black pepper into a plastic-lidded
screwtop jar, blender or food
processor. Shake, blend or whizz
to an emulsion. Refrigerate. Shake
before use.

Additions: 2tbsp freshly chopped
tarragon; a pinch of powdered
saffron; 2 garlic cloves, crushed;
1tsp tomato purée with a little
dried crushed chilli, and 1tbsp
each chopped fresh coriander,
spring onion and ginger shreds.

PEANUT & COCONUT DRESSING

THIS DIPPABLE, POURABLE, SPREADABLE DRESSING IS PERFECT FOR RICE,
NOODLES AND VEGETABLE SNACKS. YOU CAN EITHER SERVE IT HOT OR COLD, AND BECAUSE IT
KEEPS WELL IT IS EASY TO MAKE SURE THERE IS ALWAYS SOME TO HAND.

CALORIES PER SERVING (1TBSP EACH): 35
SERVES: 16

In a blender or food processor,
combine 2tbsp each light soy sauce
and peanut butter. Add 2tsp dark
sesame oil, ½ tsp each sweet chilli
sauce and ground cumin, and a
5cm/2in piece of fresh root ginger,
grated. Add 150ml/¼ pint canned

coconut cream, stirred, and
150ml/¼ pint boiling water. Blend
or whizz for 2–3 minutes or until
completely creamy.

Use warm or else refrigerate.
This dressing should keep well for
up to 10 days.

CHEAT'S LOWER-FAT DRESSING

CALORIES PER TABLESPOON: 63
MAKES: 300ML/½ PINT

A home-made mayonnaise stand-in.

Combine 225g/8oz very-low-fat
soft cheese, 1tbsp each of lemon
juice and Dijon mustard, a pinch
of seasalt and 6 tbsp of virgin olive
oil in a food processor or bowl.
Whizz or whisk until creamy.
Trickle in 8tbsp boiling water
gradually, whisking constantly, to
make a glossy sauce. Refrigerate
for up to 2 weeks.
Aioli-style: add 6–8 garlic cloves,
crushed.
Rouille-style: add 1tsp hot paprika
to Aioli-style.
Seafood dressing: add 1tbsp tomato
purée, the grated zest and juice

of ½ orange and 1tsp harissa (hot
chilli paste).
Tartare sauce: add 2tbsp each of
pickled capers, chopped gherkins
and fresh dill and parsley.

Peanut & Coconut Dressing with noodles and vegetables

Pesto with Pistachios

BEST EVER BÉCHAMEL SAUCE

CALORIES PER SERVING: 105
SERVES: 4

Microwaved béchamel (or white sauce, a more accurate description) is velvety and good. It tastes less of scorched milk and more of the milk itself. Sweeten it or add spicy, savoury additions for whatever effect you wish.

25g/1oz salted butter or
2tbsp olive oil
2tbsp plain flour
150ml/¼ pint skimmed milk
4tbsp low-fat natural
bio-yogurt

Put the butter (or oil) in a 600ml/ 1 pint microwave-proof measuring jug or small high-sided bowl.

Microwave, uncovered, on HIGH for 30 seconds. Add the flour and microwave on HIGH for another 30 seconds. Add the milk, whisk and microwave on HIGH for 2 minutes. Whisk and microwave for another minute. Whisk in the yogurt, then use hot, warm or cold. Add flavourings or use plain.

CORIANDER GUACAMOLE

CALORIES PER SERVING (2TBSP EACH): 98
MAKES: 600ML/1 PINT

VARIATION
Add seeded tomato in small dice.

Scrape the flesh of 2 soft, ripe Hass avocados into a food processor bowl. Add 2 chopped spring onions, the shredded zest and juice of 1 lime, 8g/¼ oz fresh coriander, ½ tsp seasalt flakes, and 8tbsp low-calorie mayonnaise. Whizz to a creamy purée.

Cover and keep refrigerated for up to 1 week.

PESTO WITH PISTACHIOS

GLORIOUS, CONCENTRATED HOME-MADE PESTO ENHANCES PASTA,
SANDWICHES OR CRUDITÉ-TYPE SUMMER MEALS. IT ALSO TRANSFORMS VEGETABLE SOUP.
IT BEATS MOST BOUGHT VARIETIES HANDS DOWN!

CALORIES PER 2 TEASPOONS: 48
MAKES: 275G/10OZ

Dilute it if wished with a little boiling water (or oil) at serving time.

125g/4oz shelled salted pistachios
50g/2oz chunk of Parmesan cheese
85g/3oz fresh basil leaves
(i.e. 3–4 supermarket-size plants)
25g/1oz fresh parsley
4 large garlic cloves, crushed
4tbsp extra virgin olive oil
4 tbsp dry white wine
freshly ground black pepper
(optional)

Microwave the nuts on HIGH on a large, uncovered microwave-proof platter for 6 minutes, stirring from sides to centre 3 times during cooking. Shake well so that the skins flake off.

Using the grater attachment of a food processor, grate the cheese coarsely (or hand grate). Replace the chopping blade and add the nuts, herbs (torn) and garlic. Process in short bursts to a crumbly texture. Trickle in the oil and wine gradually, with the machine running, to give a dense green paste.

To make by hand, pound the nuts in a generous-sized mortar and pestle then add the cheese, torn herbs and garlic and pound to a crumbly mass. Slowly trickle in the oil and wine, pounding to a paste.

Season, transfer to a pot and keep, covered, in the refrigerator for up to 2 weeks.

TAPENADE WITH MUSHROOMS

CLASSIC OLIVE PASTE LIGHTENED WITH MUSHROOMS AND LEMON.
GOOD FOR RICE, PASTA, POLENTA TOPPINGS AND SANDWICHES,
AND ON TOAST OR CRACKERS.

CALORIES PER SERVING: 59
SERVES: 8

In a food processor or large mortar, combine: 100g/3½ oz black olives, stoned and chopped; 2 garlic cloves, crushed; 50g/2oz button or field mushrooms, chopped; and 6 canned anchovy fillets, drained and scissor-chopped. Process or pound to a dry, grainy paste. Add 2tbsp low-fat mayonnaise, the juice of 1 lemon and 15g/½ oz scissor-chopped fresh parsley. Process or pound again. Refrigerate in a lidded pot or jar for up to 4 days.

TWO-MINUTE SMOKED SALMON DIP

A 'HEART-HEALTHY' DIP, TOPPING OR SPREAD FOR BREAKFAST TOAST
OR OPEN SANDWICHES. IT IS ALSO DELICIOUS SERVED AS AN ACCOMPANIMENT
TO RAW CRISP VEGETABLES.

CALORIES PER SERVING: 50
SERVES: 8

Put 225g/8oz smoked salmon, chopped, into a food processor with the juice of 1 blood orange, 100g/3½oz low-fat soft cheese and 1tsp crushed pink peppercorns. Whizz to a rough paste. Refrigerate in a lidded pot for up to 10 days.

RADISHES ON ICE

PERFECT CRISP RADISHES HAVE A CLEAN TASTE AND A PEPPERY CRUNCH
AND ARE ALMOST A HEALTH TONIC. THEY LOOK BEAUTIFUL BUT HAVE ALMOST NO CALORIES.
SERVE THEM WASHED BUT WHOLE, SINCE THE LEAVES CAN ALSO BE EATEN AS SALAD.

CALORIES PER SERVING: 25
SERVES: 4

VARIATION
Slice a crusty baguette wafer thin. Serve in a basket with radishes and their dips to make instant sandwiches, with low-fat soft cheese, Harissa Curd or Tandoori Cheese Dip (page 124).

Wash and dry 2 bunches of pink radishes or French pink and white 'breakfast radishes'. Divide into 4 smaller bunches. Tie with ribbon and set each bunch on some crushed ice. Have 4 individual flat dishes for Popped Spice Salt Seasoning (page 125), and some seasalt flakes for dipping.

TWO-MINUTE SMOKED SALMON DIP

TANDOORI CHEESE DIP

AN UNORTHODOX CHEESE MIXTURE WITH A REAL, SPICY BITE.
KEEP SOME IN YOUR FRIDGE FOR USE WITH CRACKERS, JACKET POTATOES, POPPADUMS,
PURIS, TOAST OR CELERY STICKS.

CALORIES PER SERVING: 86
SERVES: 8

Put 2 crushed garlic cloves, 4 chopped spring onions, 150g/5oz grated Red Leicester cheese and 50g/2oz ripe Brie, chopped, into a food processor or large bowl. Add 4tbsp boiling water. Process (or mix) to a sticky ball. Add 1tsp crushed pink peppercorns and ½ tsp tandoori spice seasoning.

Process again in bursts (or mix thoroughly) to a rosy paste. Spoon into a lidded pot and refrigerate for up to 10 days.

INSTANT TZATZIKI

CALORIES PER SERVING: 115
SERVES: 1

Ever-useful, this has an authentic taste of village Greece.

Coarsely grate 100g/3½ oz cucumber, skin and all, into a non-metal sieve. Squeeze hard to extract the juice. Add 1tsp salt, stir and leave for 5 minutes, then squeeze again. Add to a bowl with 15g/½ oz fresh mint, chopped, and 2 garlic cloves, crushed.

Stir in 5tbsp of thick Greek cow's milk yogurt. It should keep for 2−3 days if you cover and refrigerate it.

HARISSA CURD

A ROSY PINK, SAVOURY SPICED SPREAD.
GOOD FOR REPLACING BUTTER ON JACKET POTATOES, VEGETABLES *AU NATUREL*
AND FLATBREADS OR CRACKERS.

CALORIES PER SERVING: 28
SERVES: 8

Put 1tsp harissa (hot chilli paste), ¼ tsp tandoori seasoning, 2tsp extra virgin olive oil, 2 garlic cloves, crushed, 1tsp light soy sauce and 100g/3½ oz low-fat soft cheese into a bowl. Stir until smooth. Refrigerate for up to 2 weeks.

POPPED SPICE SALT SEASONING

NUTS GIVE THIS HOT-SALT-SOUR SEASONING ITS BALANCE. IT'S A UNITED NATIONS
OF A SEASONING: BASED ON TSIRE, A NIGERIAN PEANUT-CHILLI MIX, IT ALSO CONTAINS CARIBBEAN,
ASIAN AND INDIAN INGREDIENTS.

**CALORIES PER SERVING (½ TSP EACH): 10
MAKES:** 188G/6½ OZ

Besides salt and chillies the other spices
are: black onion seeds (nigella); spicy
pink peppercorns, now from the Antilles;
sumac, from Central Asia, a deep red
astringent powder; and amchur, which is
powdered unripe mango. Although you
will have to search for the necessary
exotics in Afro-Caribbean, Asian and
Middle Eastern grocers, this happy
mélange is certainly worth the effort.

125g/4oz dry roasted peanuts
25g/1oz pink peppercorns
25g/1oz seasalt flakes
1tbsp dried crushed chillies
1tbsp black onion seeds (nigella)
1tbsp sumac
1tbsp amchur

Preheat a browning dish in the
microwave for about 4–5 minutes
or until moderately hot (or
according to the manufacturer's
instructions). Quickly add the
first 3 ingredients. Cover and
microwave on HIGH for 2 minutes
or until faint popping sounds
and a delicious aroma are both
noticeable; halfway through,

stir from the edges to the centre.
Stir in the remaining ingredients,
mixing well.

Using an electric coffee grinder
or pestle and mortar, grind half
the mixture to a coarse powder,
then mix in with the unground
remainder. Leave to cool
completely.

Pack into clean, dry decorative
pots or jars that can go straight to
the table. Store in a cool, dark, dry
place. Use ½ tsp or so per serving
at the table to enliven plain, bland
foods such as rice, noodles or
mashed root vegetables that you
might otherwise have been
tempted to pile butter on.

HONG KONG FIRECRACKER SAUCE

SHOCK YOUR TASTE BUDS INTO ACTION WITH THIS HIGHLY OPINIONATED
CONDIMENT. DELICIOUS WHETHER USED ON THE SIDE OF THE PLATE OR
OVER NOODLES, SEAFOOD OR RICE.

**CALORIES PER TABLESPOON: 52
SERVES:** 10 (MAKES 150ML/¼ PINT)

2.5cm/1in piece of fresh root ginger,
finely shredded
2tsp crushed garlic or garlic purée
1tbsp groundnut oil
6tbsp dry sherry
6tbsp white wine vinegar
175g/6oz reduced-sugar apricot jam
1 large dried red chilli, seeded and
crushed
1tsp light soy sauce

Put the ginger, garlic and oil in a
microwave-proof measuring jug,
bowl or ring dish. Microwave,
uncovered, on HIGH for 1 minute.

Take out of the oven and stir
well. Then add the sherry, vinegar,
jam, chilli and soy sauce. Stir
again. Microwave, uncovered, on
HIGH for a further 3 minutes or
until the mixture is hot and
bubbling and the chilli skin looks
rehydrated.

Use hot, warm or cold (keep
sauce refrigerated). It makes a
splendid dipping sauce for dim
sum, prawns, crisps, crackers or
stuffed celery. Eat with caution,
however, as it is very hot.

INDEX

BIBLIOGRAPHY

Cless, Traude & Maier-Leibnitz, Heinz, *Principles of Microwave Cooking.* Oxford Symposium on Food & Cookery, 1985.

Coenders, A, *The Chemistry of Cooking.* The Parthenon Publishing Group Ltd, Carnforth, UK, 1992.

Cost, Bruce, *Foods from the Far East.* Random Century, London, 1990.

Coultate, T.P., *Food: The Chemistry of Its Components.* Royal Society of Chemistry, London, 1988.

C.O.M.A. Report, DHSS Committee on the Medical Aspects of Food Policy, London.

Dickenson, Donald, *How to Fortify Your Immune System.* Arlington Books, London, 1984.

Drummond, Vastano & Vastano, *Cook's Healthy Handbook.* John Wiley & Sons Inc., 1992.

Ferguson, Clare, *Gourmet Vegetarian Microwave Cookery.* Grub Street, London, 1986

Ferguson, Clare, *Microwave Cooking A La Carte.* Grub Street, London, 1990.

Food Safety Questions and Answers. Food Safety Advisory Centre, London.

Health of the Nation, DHSS.

Holford, Patrick, *The Energy Equation.* I.O.N. Press, London, 1988.

Jaffrey, Madhur, *Far Eastern Cookery.* BBC Books, London, 1989.

Jerome, Carl, *The Good Health Microwave Cookbook.* Bantam Books, 1990.

Jester, Pat, *Microwave Cookbook, The Complete Guide.* HP Books, Tucson, USA, 1983.

Kafka, Barbara, *Microwave Gourmet.* William Morrow & Co. Inc., New York, 1987.

Kafka, Barbara, *Microwave Gourmet Health Style Cookbook.* Barrie & Jenkins, London 1990.

Le Fanu, James, *Eat Your Heart Out.* Macmillan, London 1987.

Leigh, Lis, *The Sunday Times Guide to Enlightened Eating.* Century, London, 1986.

McGee, Harold, *The Curious Cook.* HarperCollins, New York, 1992.

McGee, Harold, *On Food and Cooking.* Charles Scribner's Sons. New York, 1984.

N.A.C.N.E. Report. *Proposals for Nutritional Guidelines for Health Education in Britain.* 1983.

Paul, A. A. & Southgate D. A. T., *McCance & Widdowson's: The Composition of Foods.* HMSO, 1988. (See later supplements also.)

Reader's Digest Microwave Cookbook. Dorling Kindersley, London, 1990.

Roden, Claudia, *A New Book of Middle Eastern Food.* Penguin Books, London, 1986.

Sanders, Tom & Bazalgette, Peter, *The Food Revolution.* Bantam Press, 1991.

van Straten, Michael & Griggs, Barbara, *Superfoods.* Dorling Kindersley, London, 1991.

Wills, Judith, *Slim and Healthy Mediterranean Cooking.* Conran Octopus, London, 1992.

AUTHOR'S ACKNOWLEDGEMENTS

Thanks to Christopher Robbins, for his valued advice, continuing support, and wit. Catherine Brown, whose comments continually cheered me on. Louise Simpson, my long-suffering and dedicated editor. Anne Furniss and Mary Evans, whose faith in my ideas made this project possible. David Gill, for his impassioned photography, and his assistant Paul Ashley, for his enthusiastic help. Katherine Harris, for her inspired assistance during the long days of photography. Helen Payne, for her wonderful photographic props. Alyson Kyles for her design expertise. Graeme Harris, for my jacket portrait.